ABILITY STRUCTURE

AND SUBGROUPS

IN MENTAL RETARDATION

Johs. Clausen, Ph. D.

Department of Research

The Training School at Vineland

SPARTAN BOOKS
Washington

MACMILLAN AND CO., LTD.
London

JOHS. CLAUSEN, the author of *Ability Structure and Subgroups in Mental Retardation*, was born in Bergen, Norway. There he graduated from the Gymnasium and then went to the University of Kiel in Germany to study sociology. From 1933 to 1938 he majored in psychology at the University of Oslo, winning the degree of magister artium. Two years later, Professor Clausen received a research grant to study respiration movements of psychiatric patients at Ulleval Hospital in Oslo.

A fellowship from the Norwegian government for work in experimental pyschology brought the author to the United States in 1947. Other Research Fellowships followed, including a period at Columbia University, New York, and work with Dr. Carney Landis at the Department of Research Psychology, New York State Psychiatric Institute.

In 1955 Dr. Clausen came to The Training School at Vineland in New Jersey; he became Chief of Psychological Research in 1957 and Research Administrator in 1961. Among his other accomplishments, he numbers two monographs, some twenty-seven journal articles on aspects of mental retardation, and grant awards from both the National Science Foundation and the National Institutes of Health.

It was at the famous Training School at Vineland that Professor Clausen, in company with his associates, began the seven years of research that culminate in the results reported in this book. Taking a new approach to the problem of differentiating between retardation of genetic origin and that caused by organic factors, the researchers attempted to subdivide retardates into homogeneous subgroups on the basis of structure of ability. Dr. Clausen studied 275 retardates ranging in age from eight to twenty-four years and administered thirty-four different tests in the domains of sensory, motor, perceptual, and complex mental functions.

Dr. Clausen and his co-workers found that, significantly, there are no systematic differences between groups of retardates which can be related to etiological categories. The detailed accounts of the tests and the tables of results revealed in this volume will have great influence on the future of educational programs and will light the way to greater and more definitive research in the still-unknown depths of mental retardation.

The Foschi Studio

Library of Congress Catalog Card Number 65-28297

PRINTED IN THE UNITED STATES OF AMERICA

Sole distributors in Great Britain, the British Commonwealth and the Continent of Europe:

MACMILLAN AND COMPANY, LTD.
Little Essex Street
London W.C.2

SPARTAN BOOKS 1250 Connecticut Avenue, N. W.,
Washington, D. C.

Table of Contents

PREFACE

It is primarily for practical reasons that The Ability Structure Project is presented under a single authorship. Actually, it is the result of the labors of a sizable team. First of all, credit goes to my associates during the seven years through which the project lasted: Dr. Noel Jenkin designed some of the tests, polished the test procedures, and wrote and revised the test instructions until they reached their final form; Dr. Sheldon Rosenberg, in a later phase, supervised the routine data collection work, prepared and supervised the statistical analysis, and prepared the initial interpretation of the traditional factor analysis; Mr. Rathe Karrer has been of immeasurable value in preparing the manuscript by constantly improving the reasoning and the interpretation of the data and making the presentation more concise and cohesive.

In spite of the assistance of these three colleagues, any shortcomings of the study must remain my own responsibility.

Also to be acknowledged are the research assistants who have shown a remarkable dedication and patience in the demanding task of administering a battery of 33 tests to a total of 388 subjects, three-fourths of whom were retarded. The assistants who worked in the project were: Mr. Richard Gibson, Dr. Ethel Weiss, Mrs. Sally Feallock, Mrs. Kari Tangevold Juhaz, Mrs. Dagne Poruks, Mr. John Tringo, Mrs. Jih Jie Chang and Mr. David Hoats. Mrs. Dagne Poruks has stayed with the project to the very end, and in addition to administering the battery, she has performed numerous other tasks, including follow-up statistical analyses and preparation of tables and graphs. Added to this list of assistants should be Mrs. Jean Lindsley and Miss Joan Presti, who recorded the EEGs of the retarded children.

Anyone who has prepared a manuscript appreciates the value of a secretary who can cheerfully cope with the seemingly unending series of revisions which occur from the first draft to the printer's copy. This Mrs. Helen Allonardo contributed, and in addition, she kept track of subjects and schedules, data and bills.

We are indebted to our consultants who assisted us most effectively in the various tasks: Dr. Charles E. Henry of Cleveland Clinic, Cleveland, Ohio, interpreted all the EEG records; Dr. Geraldine King, Department of Neurology, University of Pennsylvania, conducted all the neurological examinations; and Dr. John DeCani, Statistics Department, University of Pennsylvania, generously gave of his time to try to fill some of the holes in our statistical knowledge. Toward the end, Dr. David Saunders of Princeton helped us with advice and did some of the computer work for us.

Gratitude is due to the superintendents and staffs of the various institutions from which our populations were drawn. Not only were we given permission to work with the children, but we were provided space to set up our equipment and assisted in selecting our subjects. Thus, we wish to thank Dr. Joseph J. Parnicky and Dr. Leonard S. Blackman of E. R. Johnstone Training and Research Center, Bordentown, N. J.; Mr. Philip S. Thomas and Dr. Erwin Friedman of the State Colony at New Lisbon, N. J.; Mr. Frederick Klaumizter and Dr. Samuel Babcock of Vineland State School, Vineland, N. J.; Dr. Claude E. Richardson and Dr. Douglas T. Davidson of Elwyn Training School, Elwyn, Pa.; and Mr. Edward L. Johnstone and Dr. Mortimer Garrison, Jr. of the Woods Schools, Langhorne, Pa. Also, we appreciate the cooperation of Mr. A. L. Donley, former Superintendent of Schools in Vineland, and of the three school principals, Mr. John Richards, Mr. Caro Ricci and Mr. C. J. Schoendorf, Jr., who made it possible to recruit the normal sample.

My wife, Martha M. Clausen, has valiantly tried to uphold standard usage of the English language and I wish to thank her for her assistance in polishing the manuscript.

Finally, we are sincerely grateful to the Director of The Training School at Vineland, Dr. Walter Jacob, for the consistent support he has given throughout the project.

And now when others have been acknowledged, it remains only to say "Thank You" to the nearly 400 children, retarded or normal, who served as subjects in the study.

The Ability Structure Project was supported financially by Grant M-1394, from the National Institute of Mental Health.

Johs. Clausen,
Vineland, N. J.

I INTRODUCTION

In current practice, IQ and etiology are the primary bases for classification of the population variously called mentally retarded, mentally deficient, or mentally defective.[1] The degree to which an individual is defined or categorized by these dimensions (i.e., the extent to which it is possible to predict behavior) is, however, highly questionable. The IQ is characteristically an average of several disparate functions and may thus obscure significant constellations of functions involved. Also, standard intelligence tests sample only a very limited number and variety of abilities. It should be clear to anyone who has had any intimate day by day contact with the retardates that two individuals who are both classified as functioning at a moderately retarded level can differ strikingly along a variety of behavioral dimensions. Profile analysis of subscale items among individuals with identical IQs has also been claimed to reveal diverse patterns (e.g., Wechsler, 1944; Beck & Lam, 1955; Baroff, 1959; Satter, 1955). Many authors (e.g., Doll, 1946; Tredgold, 1947; Penrose, 1949; and Clarke & Clarke, 1958) have discussed the hazards of defining retardation in terms of IQ alone. Traditionally, the tendency has been to supplement IQ with consideration of "social adequacy" rather than with more extensive appraisal of psychological functions and their patterning. Thus, consideration of ability profiles based on a wide variety of functions seems indicated.

Etiological dichotomies, such as *organic-familial* or *endogenous-exogenous,* also present problems. These terms are clearly lacking in specificity. *Organic* may refer to anything which has an impact on the biological system, regardless of mode of action, locus or extent. Why such individuals should be expected to exhibit behavioral uniformity is therefore not easy to understand. *Familial* may imply a genetic condition or the outcome of cultural factors or an interaction of both. It is not surprising then, that attempts to differentiate between familials and organics in terms of behavioral characteristics have often produced negative or uninterpretable results (e.g., Galla-

[1] The term *mentally retarded* has generally been used in this study since it seems to be the most accepted. Arguments against this term will be presented later.

gher, 1957; Barnett, Ellis, & Pryer, 1960). There is, of course, the possibility that physiologically there is little difference between retardation due to certain kinds of organic insult and retardation of genetic origin and maybe even retardation resulting from cultural factors. While biochemistry and genetics have succeeded in differentiating certain clinical types and have made a beginning toward uncovering the physiological correlates of such conditions (e.g., the additional chromosome in mongolism, excess of phenylalanine in phenylketonuria), the number of retardates which can be so differentiated accounts for no more than a small percentage of the total population of defectives. We are aware of no serious attempts to differentiate these groups in terms of psychological abilities.

Another dichotomy which has gained considerable popularity is the distinction made between the so-called "trainables" and "educables." While there have been attempts to employ a variety of measures in making such predictions, these terms are still without any reliable degree of specificity, and as used today they represent hardly anything more than an arbitrary cutoff point on the IQ continuum. The practical need, nevertheless, to develop assessment instruments which will predict to what extent an individual can benefit from a given educational or training program, is a continuing one. A more extensive appraisal of ability structure may serve this purpose better than IQ alone, and definition of homogeneous subgroups may contribute significantly to this task.

In view of the wide variety of causal factors related to retardation, it seems reasonable to raise the question as to whether they are manifested in differential constellations of impaired and intact functions. The hypothesis basic to this study is that the mentally retarded represent a diversity of functional problems, and that they may be differentiated into subgroups on the basis of psychological functions. Abilities have been explored in a hierarchy of functions from basic sensory and motor tasks, through perceptual functions to reasoning, memory, and integrative functions as they are represented in standard intelligence scales. A comprehensive mapping of these psychological functions which underlie intellectual development was attempted, and these functions were measured in relatively pure form as well as in various degrees of interaction to form a continuum of complexities. Because of the scarcity of experimental studies in retardation, little background information was available for the task of selecting tests to be included in the present study.

The question will be no doubt raised as to why the problem of personality structure has been neglected. The answer is that while it was tempting to include personality measures, it was felt that the present state of knowledge of personality dynamics in mental retardation argued against such a venture. It was also felt that the probability of success of this initial venture would be increased by including only measures which would produce quantitative data.

An attempt to differentiate retardates in terms of functional rather than etiological characteristics should have important practical consequences for future research relative to educational programs. If one can differentiate subgroups on the basis of ability structure, this should provide an opportunity for the educators to design training programs which take into account the special needs of the group. More basically, however, any reduction in group variability in homogeneous groupings would facilitate immeasurably the interpretation of results of experimental studies. It might well be that similar hypotheses would apply to other disciplines concerned with mental retardation, such as neurophysiology or biochemistry. If similar approaches were adopted by these disciplines, fascinating opportunities for studying the relationship between biological and psychological functioning might open up.

The guiding hypothesis of the present study is that subgroups of the retardates can be identified empirically on the basis of intra-individual performances that indicate a variety of patterns of sensory, perceptual, motor, and complex mental abilities or functions. For this purpose, inverse factor analysis and syndrome analysis were used. It was anticipated, however, that traditional factor analysis of test intercorrelations would assist in mapping the ability domains of the retarded. It was decided, therefore, that a maximum amount of information would be obtained by using traditional as well as inverse factor analysis. The possible uses of factor analysis for purposes of classification have been sorely neglected in the area of mental retardation (Sarason & Gladwin, 1959) while they have been more extensively appropriated in other areas of psychopathology (e.g., Eysenck, 1961).

While the term mentally retarded implies deviating developmental trends, developmental studies of these subjects are very scarce. The present study considers whether different functions have different rates of development, and whether development in retardates is characterized by a delayed progress up to a normal level or by an early termination of progress. Developmental trends were studied on a heterogeneous group of subjects, but, to the extent that one is able to define functional subgroups, developmental trends should eventually be investigated in each subgroup separately. Also, longitudinal studies would be preferable to cross-sectional sampling.

In addition to the psychological tests, each retarded subject was given a neurological and EEG examination, and information about family, medical, and developmental history was obtained from the subject's record. This information was necessary for traditional classification on etiological grounds, so that these groups could be compared among themselves and comparisons made between results of this study and the traditional groupings. Furthermore, such information would afford the opportunity for some initial comparisons between psychological traits and biological functioning. The findings of these comparisons will be reported in a subsequent article. Beyond an interest in biological variables for their possible classificatory values, there is a strong possibility of contributing to the understanding of biological functioning in the normal organism. This is an aspect of research in mental retardation which may deserve more attention than it has heretofore received.

In summary, then, it was the purpose of the present study to attempt to map ability structure of the retardates and to define subgroups of the retarded on the basis of constellations of impaired and intact functions. A second purpose was to compare psychological functions and their interactions in mentally retarded children at various age levels, in an effort to study the development of ability structures, an area which is virtually unexplored. In addition to providing the basis for a classification system and paving the way for differential pedagogical methods, such a survey should afford the opportunity to compare ability structure to known organic damage and physiological dysfunctioning.

More specifically the objectives of the study may be outlined as follows:

1. To assemble normative data for a wide variety of basic psychological functions which in the past have not been systematically investigated among the mentally retarded.
2. To provide new understanding of the ability structure in the mentally retarded and to relate this structure to physical and intellectual development; i.e., to chronological and mental age.
3. To differentiate the mentally retarded into subgroups which are psychologically and behaviorally more homogeneous than those provided by current classification systems. Incidentally, such groupings should provide criterion populations which are more suitable for validating diagnostic instruments.

4. To relate configuration of abilities with extent of central nervous system damage as indicated by medical, neurological, and EEG examinations.
5. To relate the factors underlying the groupings of Objective No. 3 to etiology as is presumed from medical and family history.
6. To provide the raw materials which may make possible the development of new diagnostic tools and to provide new ways of combining results of existing tests to achieve maximum diagnostic power.
7. To extend and improve instrumentation for more effectively discriminating between individuals within the groupings defined in Objective 3.

II TEST PROCEDURE

DEVELOPMENT OF THE TEST BATTERY AND SCORING SYSTEM

Once the decision had been made that the Ability Structure Battery should include a hierarchy of sensory, motor, perceptual, and intellectual measures, the following factors were considered in selecting the tests:

1. The task could be completed at an MA level of four and still discriminate at an MA level of approximately 12 years.
2. The instructions would be understood by retarded children with an MA of four years.
3. The total testing time would be limited to a maximum of about 10 hours.

Very limited information was available from the existing literature concerning which tasks mentally retarded children can and can not do. To a large extent educated guesses had to be made as to which tests were suitable for inclusion in the Battery. From a test administration point of view, it appeared that the initial selection was rather successful. A group of 31 retarded girls within the same age and IQ range as the experimental population served as a pilot group. Although test instruction and scoring procedures were modified as a result of experiences with the pilot group, it was not found necessary to exclude any of the tests which were originally selected. The two tests which caused the most difficulty were visual acuity (Orthorater) and perimetry. Many children seemed to lack the concept of direction to indicate the location of the test object in the Orthorater test. By patiently explaining what *up, down, right,* and *left* referred to, it was possible to carry most of the subjects through. True pathological visual fields were encountered in only two cases. The main difficulty with the perimeter test seemed to be the task of looking at the fixation point and simultaneously attending to the test object in the periphery. In a large number of cases, the perimeter chart indicated a severe bilateral restriction (20°) of circular shape. From other observations, it appeared that the visual fields of most of these subjects were not that restricted and therefore probably represented artifacts. Such cases were so numerous that it was decided to leave the perimeter data out of the analysis.

The battery consisted of 33 tests (numbered arbitrarily from 1 to 33). Initially, an attempt was made to derive as many scores from each test as possible. In those tests which consisted of a number of trials, the range was computed as a measure of variability. This gave a total of 124 scores. All the scores of each subject were transferred from the raw data sheets to a master card which is reproduced in Fig. 1.

The V column on the card contains the subscores of the tests in numerical order and the T column refers to the test number. It may be noted that PMA is Test No. 21. The X column contains the overall score for a particular test, such as mean, total correct, median, etc., as the case may be in accordance with the information presented in the section on Description of the Tests. The R column shows the range of the scores, most often the highest score minus the lowest or a mean of one series minus the mean of another. In many cases it was not possible to obtain a range, such instances being indicated by a bar in the R-column. The E (evaluation) column contains the overall estimate by the examiner of the subject's test performance, in terms of factors which might interfere with performance. How this overall estimation was arrived at and coded is explained below.

V 90, Phosphene Threshold, was not routinely recorded for the subjects and will not be reported here. Correlations between phosphene threshold and scores from the Ability Structure Project Battery were obtained on 49 cases and have been reported separately by Clausen and Karrer (1961).

V 91, Project Group, indicates the code number of the institution where the subject was residing and served primarily the purpose of administrative convenience. Items V 92 to 98 were included because this information was directly available from the files of the children from The Training School at Vineland. Such information was not always available from other institutions and these variables were therefore excluded from the general data analysis. Etiology was determined in accordance with the Riggs and Rain classification system (1952a and 1952b). Descriptions of neurological and EEG examinations and their coding appear in separate sections below.

Following the collection of the data an attempt was made to systematically reduce the number of scores to a more manageable and discriminative set. This reduction was achieved primarily by: 1: Scatter diagrams between pairs of measures from a particular test

Name: 4. Institution: 3. Sex: 2. Age: 1. Subject #

V	T	Description	X	R	E	V	T	Description	X	R	E
5	1	Knowledge, L, R		—		25	3	Acuity, overall		—	
6	1	Hand pref.		—		26	3	Color		—	
7	1	Handwriting		—		27	4	Apprehension		—	
8	1	Tapping		—		28	5	Pegboard, right		—	
9	1	Monocular		—		29	5	Pegboard, left		—	
10	1	Binocular		—		30	5	Pegboard, both		—	
11	1	Hand dominance		—		31	5	Peg. composite		—	
12	1	Eye dominance		—		32	6	Recognition		—	
13	2	Grip, left				33	7	Time est. median			
14	2	Grip, right				34	7	Time est. Av. err.			
15	2	Grip, both				35	8	Word association			
16	3	Phoria, vert. far		—		36	9	Speech, score		—	
17	3	Phoria, vert. near		—		37	9	Speech, loss db		—	
18	3	Phoria, lat. far		—		38	10	Railwalking T		—	
19	3	Phoria, lat. near		—		39	10	Railwalking P		—	
20	3	Phoria, overall		—		40	11	Porteus MA		—	
21	3	Acuity, bin. far		—		41	11	Porteus IQ		—	
22	3	Acuity, bin. near		—		42	12	2 point, left			
23	3	Acuity, right, far		—		43	12	2 point, right			
24	3	Acuity, left, far		—		44	12	2 point, mean			

V	T	Description	X	R	E	V	T	Description	X	R	E
45	13	Lower Arm				65	26	Flicker fusion			
46	14	Identification				66	27	RT scrambled			
47	15	Audio. left				67		66 minus 50			
48	15	Audio. right				68	28	Weight lifting			
49	15	Audio. binaural				69	29	Hand pres. hits			
50	16	Visual RT				70	29	Hand pres. error			
51	17	Brightness, error				71	29	Hand pres. RT			
52	17	Brightness, MD				72	30	Ataxiometry M			
53	18	Auditory RT				73	30	Ataxiometry L			
54	19	Stereognosis		—		74	30	Ataxiometry Tot.			
55	20	Mirror T error t				75	31	Perimetry, left		—	
56	20	Mirror T errors				76	31	Perimetry, right		—	
57	20	Mirror T time				77	31	Perim. overall		—	
58	20	Mirror AT error t				78	32	Muller L. extent			
59	20	Mirror AT errors				79	32	Muller L. antic.			
60	20	Mirror AT time				80	33	Azimuth, arith.		—	
61	22	RT Pictures				81	33	Azimuth, algeb.		—	
62	23	Tapping				82	33	Azimuth, Rot. diff.		—	
63	24	Raven		—		83	33	Azimuth, Reversal		—	
64	25	Auditory choice									

V	T	Description	X	R	E	V	Classification	Code
84	34	Kines. L, error				91	Project group	
85	34	Kines. L, MD				92	Personality	
86	34	Kines. R, error				93	Physico-psychological	
87	34	Kines. R, MD				94	Present intell. level	
88	34	Kines. both, err.				95	Potential intell. level	
89	34	Kines. both, MD				96	Etiological class	
90		Phosphene thresh				97	Clinical type	
114						98	Personality disorder	
115						99	Etiology	
116						100	Neurological exam.	
117						101	EEG exam.	
118						128		
119						129		
120						130		
121						131		
122						132		
123						133		
124						134		
125						135		
126						136		
127						137		

PMA, RETARDED CASES

V	Factor	X	MA	IQ
102	V: Verbal			
103	P: Perceptual			
104	Q: Quantitative			
105	M: Motor			
106	S: Space			
107	Overall			

PMA, NORMAL CASES

108	V: Verbal			
109	S: Space			
110	R: Reasoning			
111	P: Perceptual			
112	N: Number			
113	Overall			

Figure 1. Front and back of master card on which all scores of each subject were accumulated.

and elimination of those scores for which there was a suggestion of significant correlation; 2. The obtaining of reliability coefficients for all those scores where it was possible to compute a split-half correlation (product-moment) and elimination of all scores with nonsignificant coefficients. The reliability coefficient was determined from a group of sixty retarded and sixty normal subjects chosen at random from the total samples for each group. With an N of 60, an r of .22 and above is significant at the .05 level. Other factors which were considered for reducing the battery were a very narrow distribution of the scores, and extreme difficulties encountered by the retarded subjects in understanding the instructions and carrying out the tasks. In this way, the fifty measures (or variables) plus CA, listed in Table 1, were arrived at. The table shows a descriptive title of the test, the nature of the scores, an indication of whether "good" per-

TABLE 1

VARIABLES INCLUDED IN THE FINAL ANALYSIS

Test		*Direction of Excellence*	*Reliability Coefficient Normals*	*Reliability Coefficient Retarded*
Lateral Dominance	hand dominance	—	—	—
	eye dominance	—	—	—
Vision	acuity	high	—	—
	color	high	—	—
Audiometry	left	low	—	—
	right	low	—	—
Speech Threshold	score	high	.62	.90
Kinesthesis	left mean deviation	low	.78	.77
	right mean deviation	low	.56	.76
Two-Point Threshold	right mean	low	.83	.83
	left mean	low	.88	.93
	difference	low	.61	.73
Ataxiometry	medial	low	.84	.96
	lateral	low	.87	.91
Grip	left mean	high	.95	.99
	right mean	high	.95	.96
Lower Arm Movement	mean	low	.92	.98
Tapping	mean	high	.91	.98
Visual Reaction Time	median	low	.89	.97
Auditory Reaction Time	median	low	.84	.96
Auditory Choice Reaction Time	median	low	.57	.81
Scrambled Foreperiod Reaction Time	median	low	.77	.93
Hand Precision	hits	high	.77	.91
	errors	low	.86	.90
Purdue Pegboard	left	high	—	—
	right	high	—	—
	both	high	—	—
Mirror Drawing	errors	low	.93	.92
	total time	low	.88	.86
	error range	low	.55	.46
Railwalking	percent of total distance	high	—	—
Word Association	median	low	.76	.84
Speed of Perception	median	low	.83	.88
Span of Apprehension	threshold	high	—	—
Identification Threshold	threshold	low	.80	.91
Recognition—non-meaningful forms	threshold	high	.45	.29
Azimuth Perception	mean deviation	low	.44	.67
	number of reversals	low	.50	.68
Brightness Discrimination	error	low	.82	.80
Critical Flicker Fusion	threshold	high	.90	.93
Stereognosis	score	high	.16	.74
Time Interval Estimation	median	500 ms	.85	.93
Weight Lifting	illusion	low	.65	.68
Muller-Lyer Illusion	extent	low	.94	.91
	anticipation	low	.84	.81
Porteus Mazes	mental age	high	—	—
	intelligence quotient	high	—	—
Raven's Matrices	score	high	.91	.77
Primary Mental Abilities	mental age	high	—	—
	intelligence quotient	high	—	—

formance is a high or a low score, and the reliability coefficient when obtainable. Direction of excellence was not applicable in some tests; e.g., Lateral Dominance. Stereognosis was allowed to remain, in spite of a reliability coefficient of .16 in the normal sample, since it measured a function (or combination of functions) which was not sampled by any of the other tests.

On the whole, the reliabilities were found to be adequately high for the retarded subjects—in some instances surprisingly high. It may be noted that the reliability coefficients for the retarded subjects were sometimes higher than for the normals, which may be due to their greater variability.

DESCRIPTION OF THE TEST BATTERY

The sequence of the tasks on the master card is arbitrary, reflecting only the order in which the tests were ready for use. In the description of the battery as well as in data presentation, the variables have been arranged in domains of functions. Lateral Dominance was considered as a background variable, with sensory, motor, perceptual, and complex mental functions as specific domains. Within each domain the variables have been arranged in what was judged to be an increasing degree of task complexity. The arrangement may be seen from the entries along the horizontal axis in Fig. 2 or from Tables 2 and 6: Variables 1-2 are background, 3-12 sensory, 13-31 motor, 32-45 perceptual, and 46-50 complex mental functions.

1. *Lateral Dominance.* This test is a shortened version of the *Harris Tests of Lateral Dominance* (1955). The following items were included:

a. Knowledge of Left and Right
b. Hand Dominance
   i Hand Preference
   ii Handwriting
   iii Tapping
c. Eye Dominance
   i Monocular Tests: Kaleidoscope, Telescope, Sight Rifle
   ii Binocular Tests: Cone, Hole

The test materials and instructions were in accordance with Harris' manual, but the scoring system was slightly different. The rating of each item was made on a five category basis as described in the manual. To obtain a numerical score, values from 0 to 4 were assigned to each of these categories so that Strong Right counted 4, Moderate Right 3, Mixed 2, Moderate Left 1, and Strong Left 0. The mean of the numerical values obtained for a subject on the three Hand Dominance sub-tests constituted the score for *Hand Dominance,* and the mean for the Monocular and Binocular tests constituted the score for *Eye Dominance.* To facilitate interpretation, a mean with a score between 0 and 1.9 was designated Left Dominance; between 2 and 2.9, Mixed Dominance; and 3 or above, Right Dominance.

The Hand and Eye Dominance Test was one of the first to be administered in the battery and a number of visual and motor tests utilized the preferred eye or hand as determined by the test.

Strength of Grip, which is an optional item in Harris' battery, was included as a separate test rather than as a laterality test.

2. *Orthorater Test.* The apparatus is described and directions for testing are given in the Bausch and Lomb Reference Manual. Uniform light conditions were maintained in the testing room by blocking out daylight and keeping the overhead light of the room on. If the subject wore glasses, the glasses were used for the acuity and color vision tests. For the purpose of this study the following three scores were utilized: (a.) Overall acuity, which is the mean of the raw score for the four acuity sub-tests; and, (b.) Color vision, which is the number of correct answers to the four numbers presented (two of which are two digit numbers).

The difficulties with the acuity tests have been mentioned above. The Orthorater tests were included primarily to obtain information about uncorrected visual impairment, so that there would be some guarantee that poor performance on subsequent visual tasks would not be the result of poor acuity. It is possible that the Orthorater, where the subject is peering into a pair of eye-pieces, provides an isolation from the surrounding, which is unfortunate for these subjects, since the examiner has less opportunity to reinforce the arousal value of the stimulus.

3. *Audiometry.* A Maico Model H-1 Audiometer, with a 28 db loss paid inserted between the output and the earphones, was used for this test. The loss pad permitted the determination of hearing thresholds for series of increasing loudness in addition to the traditional decreasing series. One ascending and one descending series was determined for each ear for the following frequencies: 125, 500, 1000, 2000, 4000, 8000, and 12000 cps. Since it was cumbersome to utilize all seven measures for each ear, percentage of hearing loss was determined with the Maico slide rule, which utilizes only four frequencies: 500, 1000, 2000, and 4000 cps. Such a score was obtained for right ear and left ear.

The scores are uncorrected for the 28 db loss pad; therefore, the hearing loss scores give relative value for our population. There is no simple conversion from the overall hearing loss score to a hearing loss score corrected for the loss pad.

4. *Threshold for Speech.* The W-1 series of the auditory test from the Central Institute for the Deaf was used, played on a Bogen Model FP17X Transcription Player. Inserted in the circuit was a voltmeter to adjust volume level for the 1000 cps calibration tone of the record, and a Hewlett-Packard Attenuator, Model 350-B, to vary the decibel level of the test series.

With one volt output and 20 db attenuation, List C was played for the subject who was asked to repeat each word to make sure that all words were understood. The first test trial utilized List A, starting at a readily audible level (usually 40 db, but modified when necessary) with attenuation increased in steps of 2 db for each successive pair of words, until the subject failed to respond to four words in succession. When this criterion was reached, the basal db value was determined from the consecutive series of plus responses (with 1 db added if it was the second word of a pair) and the number of all the remaining positive responses in the series added to the basal value.

Following the descending series an ascending series was determined using List B. The starting point was 10 db below the previously obtained threshold and again the attenuation was varied in steps of 2 db for each pair of words. The scoring method was similar to that of the descending series. The mean of the ascending and descending series constituted the score.

5. *Kinesthesis.*[2] This test measures the ability of a blindfolded subject to adjust one arm to the position of the other. The subject was seated in front of a frame containing two parallel horizontal bars extending out from him. The frame contained a chin rest which, when properly adjusted, placed the bars at eye-level. Each bar had a sliding sleeve and a centimeter ruler alongside it. The non-preferred hand gripping the slider was adjusted by means of a wooden triangle so the angle between the upper and lower arm was 115°. The slider was fastened in position and the scale reading noted. The subject was asked to grasp the

[2] The equipment for this test was designed by Dr. Noel S. Jenkin.

slider on the other side and move it along the bar until the two arms were in the same position. The position was read off to the nearest mm.

Five trials were conducted with the preferred hand, starting alternately from the near and far positions. The preferred hand was then changed to a fixed position and 10 trials were conducted with alternating starting points. Finally, 5 more trials of the original condition were conducted.

For each hand separately, the mean deviation was computed, i.e., the mean of the deviations of the separate scores from the standard value, disregarding sign.

6. *Two-Point Threshold.* A Jastrow Aesthesiometer (C. H. Stolting) was used to determine two-point thresholds on the lower part of the volar surface of each arm with the psychophysical Method of Limits. The procedure was demonstrated to the subject before he was blindfolded. Every effort was made to make the pressure uniform for all trials, the contacts simultaneous rather than successive, and applied for a constant period of 2 sec. Starting with a 4 cm distance between the two points and decreasing in steps of 5 mm, an exploratory series was carried out with the subject blindfolded, and a preliminary threshold determined. Following this, a descending test trial was conducted on the right arm, using an opening of 15 mm above the approximate threshold and decreasing by steps of 3 mm. At least two "catch" trials were included in the early part of each series. An ascending test trial was administered in a similar manner on the right arm, followed by a descending and an ascending trial on the left arm. Between each trial one minute of rest was given. After these four trials another test (Lower Arm Movement) was administered, and the subject returned for four more series: Descending Left, Ascending Left, Descending Right, and Ascending Right.

For the descending series, the first transition from a report of two to a report of one was used to determine an upper value, and the last transition from two to one to determine a lower value. The reverse was done for ascending trials. The mean of the four upper and the four lower values was determined for each arm and constituted a threshold. The following three scores were utilized: threshold for right arm, threshold for left arm, and difference between right and left thresholds.

7. *Ataxiometry.*[3] This test measures body sway in the medial and lateral planes when the blindfolded subject is standing with feet together.

A horizontal bar was rigidly fastened to a breast-plate attached to the subject with a harness. Through a system of levers, movements were transferred to a set of gear wheels, one activated by medial and the other by lateral movement. In rotating, the teeth of each gear wheel engaged the action point of a stationary relay, making an electrical contact. In this manner a series of pulses were produced which were recorded separately for medial and lateral sway on Hunter Klockounters. Four 1 min. trials were conducted, with a rest period of 1 min. between each trial, during which the blindfold was removed and the rod detached from the harness so the subject could move around.

The sensitivity of this recording technique was such that 1 cm displacement of the rod gave four counts. The following scores were used: Means of the four medial and of the four lateral counts.

8. *Strength of Grip.* For this test a Smedley Hand Dynamometer, calibrated in Kg., was used. Instructions were in accordance with Harris' Manual (1955). A group of 4 trials were run, starting with the preferred hand and alternating with the nonpreferred hand. The Orthorater Tests were then administered, following which another group of four trials was run, again alternating from preferred to nonpreferred hand. Score used: Mean of the four trials for each hand separately.

9. *Lower Arm Movement.* This test represents an attempt to measure speed of movement when the subject himself initiates the movement, rather than reacts in response to a signal. Two brass plates 3 x 3 in. were placed 10 in. apart on a wooden board. The subject was instructed to touch the two plates in suc-

[3] Credit for the design of the instrument goes largely to Mr. Richard Gibson.

cession as rapidly as possible with his dominant hand. A ground lead was attached to the subject's nondominant hand. Each brass plate was connected to a modified No. 99783 Sensitive Relay (Central Scientific Co.) which was in turn connected to a Hunter Interval Timer, so wired that it provided a holding circuit. Also inserted in the circuit was a Hunter Klockounter, Model 120. Touching the first plate activated the starting relay, which in turn activated the Klockounter. Touching the second plate activated the stopping relay which stopped the Klockounter. Thus the time in ms which elapsed between the touching of the two plates was recorded.

After five practice trials, a series of 10 test trials was recorded, the mean of which constituted the score.

10. *Tapping.* The Tapping Test is essentially the same as that used by King and Clausen (1952, 1956) and by King (1954). On a wooden board, two 3 x 3 in. brass plates were placed with 7 in. between their inner edges. Midway between the plates was a ½ in. wooden barrier. With his preferred hand, the subject touched the two plates alternately as rapidly as possible. A ground wire was fastened to the nonpreferred hand. A modified Cenco Sensitive Relay, No. 99783, inserted in the circuit, activated an impulse counter. Also in the circuit was an interval timer which permitted the recording of the number of taps made in periods of 3 sec. The subject started tapping; after two taps the 3 sec. interval was started; and after its termination the subject was asked to stop. Ten trials were included in the series, with 30 sec. rest periods between. The score was the mean of the 10 trials.

11. *Simple Visual Reaction Time.* Standard procedure was used for the measurement of simple visual reaction time. The subject released a telegraph key in response to a light signal from a neon bulb. Foreperiods varied randomly from 1 to 3 sec. The telegraph key activated a relay which controlled the circuits for the signal light and a Hunter Klockounter. The examiner's key similarly controlled simultaneously but independently both of these circuits. After 3 practice trials, 20 test trials were carried out. The subjects were closely watched during the task to be sure that they were attending to the neon bulb. Unduly long reaction times which appeared to be the result of failure of attention were discarded, and substitute trials were obtained. The score was the median of the 20 trials, expressed in ms.

12. *Simple Auditory Reaction Time.* This test was administered in the same way as Simple Visual Reaction Time. The reaction time instrument included a regular buzzer (low frequency sound) and a switch which permitted the selection of light and sound stimuli depending upon whether visual or auditory reaction time was being recorded. Visual fixation was less useful as an indication of the subject's attentiveness, but any evidence of inattention was closely watched. If such evidence coincided with any unusually long reaction times, additional trials were administered. The score consisted of the median of 20 trials in ms.

13. *Auditory Choice Reaction Time.* The reaction time apparatus provided for two auditory stimuli, a low frequency buzzer, which was used in the Simple Auditory Reaction Time Test, and a high frequency buzzer. The subject was instructed to respond to the low frequency sound but not to the high frequency sound. Foreperiods varied from 1 to 3 sec. A series consisted of 10 presentations in predetermined, random order; five low frequency and five high frequency signals. Four series were included in the test, giving a total of 20 low frequency signals to which the subject should respond. The medium of the correct responses constituted the score.

14. *Reaction Time with Prolonged Scrambled Foreperiod.* Except for the foreperiod, the procedure for this test was the same as for Simple Visual Reaction Time. Foreperiods of 2, 6, 10, and 14 sec. were used, in predetermined, random order. The series included 20 trials, with a rest period of 2 min. after the first 10. Thus each foreperiod occurred five times. The score was the mean of the 20 trials.

15. *Hand Precision.* The instrument used was the Purdue Hand Precision Test described by Tiffin (1952 pp. 139-141) and manfactured by Lafayette Instrument Company. Using the slowest rotation speed of the disc (42 RPM), the number of hits (attempts) and number of correct hits were recorded. The subject was instructed to hold the stylus in his dominant hand and try to hit the targets while following the circular movement of the disc. He was allowed to practice until he had attained a criterion of 5 correct hits in 30 sec. while following the rotating motion. The test proper consisted of six trials of 30 sec. each. Number of Correct Hits and Errors were utilized as the measures of performance.

16. *Purdue Pegboard.* The Purdue Pegboard was administered in accordance with standard instructions. The Assembly sub-test was omitted because a high correlation had been found in the pilot study between the Assembly score and the remaining scores. The three-trial version of the test was used and scores were obtained for Right hand, Left hand, and Both hands. The basic score was the number of pins placed in holes in three periods of 30 sec. each.

17. *Mirror Drawing.* The Mirror Drawing apparatus was designed for automatic recording. It is essentially a modification of the Snoddy mirror tracing instrument (Woodworth, 1938, p. 162) constructed by the Marietta Instrument Co. A six pointed brass star was surrounded by a larger brass star pattern so that there was a 1 cm separation between them. The concentric stars were placed on top of, but insulated from, a stainless steel plate, which formed the track along which the subject moved his stylus. Each side of a star point had three or four notches to prevent the subject from dragging the stylus along the sides of the star pattern. The tracing was done with a stylus which was electrically connected with the brass and the steel plates, in such a fashion that it permitted the recording of total time for tracing of the pattern (contact between the stylus and the steel plate) and number of errors in tracing the pattern (contact between stylus and brass plate).

The test was performed with the preferred hand, with the direction of movement being clockwise if the stylus was kept in the right hand, and counterclockwise if the left hand was used.

Following instructions, the subject made his first trial. If he could not complete the tracing, demonstration or additional instructions were given. The first trial without verbal or physical assistance from the examiner was counted as the first test trial, which was followed by 9 more trials, thus making a total of 10 trials.

Three scores were obtained from this test: means of the 10 trials for Error Count and Total Tracing Time (in sec.) and, as measure of variability, the mean Error Count of trials 1 and 2 minus the mean of trials 9 and 10.

18. *Railwalking.* Apparatus, instructions, and procedure for this test were described by Heath (1942). The score was the total length travelled expressed as the percentage of the possible maximum (864 in.).

19. *Word Association.* In the ASP adaptation of the Word Association test, emphasis was placed on verbal fluency rather than emotional reactions to certain words. For this purpose words which were not likely to produce emotional responses were selected from the Kent-Rosanoff test.

The subject was told that the purpose of the test was to see how quickly he could think of a word when a stimulus word was presented. Examples of various types of association were given (blackboard-chalk; street-road; dark-light) and five practice trials presented before proceeding to the test trials. For the recording, a Stolting Voice Key was used. In the rare cases where the subject had a tendency to initiate his response with an "ah," "uh," etc., and a mild suggestion to exclude the preliminary noises had no effect, the examiner used a manual key instead of the subject's microphone. If the subject failed to respond within 10 sec., the examiner proceeded to the next word. While time and response word were recorded, only median association time (in ms) for 30 test responses was utilized in the study.

20. *Verbal Reaction Time to Pictures.* In this test, a series of colored pictures of familiar objects was presented tachistoscopically, and the subject was

asked to name the picture as quickly as possible. Thus it was a test of verbal fluency, somewhat similar to our version of the Word Association test, but stimulus and response were identical.

The test utilized the tachistoscope and the voice key. The tachistoscope used for presenting the material was built on the Dodge principle, with argon-mercury lamps to illuminate the stimulus material. A Hunter Interval Timer was used to switch the light from the pre-exposure field to the exposure field and back again. The stimulus material was mounted on 8 x 5 cards. The distance from the stimulus to the eyes was 69 cm, thus providing a maximum visual angle of 16.8°. All stimulus materials were within 5.2° of visual angle, most often within 2.4°. A microphone was placed on the tachistoscope right under the aperture into which the subject was looking, and was connected to the closing relay of the voice key. The starting relay was activated by the same switch which shifted the light from the pre-exposure to the exposure side of the tachistoscope. Thus the time interval from the presentation of the picture to the verbal response could be recorded. Exposure time of the stimulus card was 2 sec. The test series consisted of 20 cards plus 10 matched substitution cards to be used when an object was misnamed. The median of 20 successful trials constituted the score.

21. *Span of Apprehension.* This is the traditional test for determining the number of dots which can be perceived in a single flash. The stimulus material was presented in the tachistoscope, using exposure intervals of 0.2 sec. For practice trials a square and a circle were presented to the subject. Following this, 14 cards, two series with one to seven dots, were presented in random order, and a preliminary threshold computed. Four series of five cards each were then presented in a prearranged random order, the number of dots depending upon the magnitude of the preliminary threshold. The relationship between preliminary threshold and the range of dots in the subsequent series was as follows:

Preliminary Threshold	Range of Dots
0–3.5	1–5
4–4.5	2–6
5–5.5	3–7
6–6.5	4–8
7	5–9

The purpose of this procedure was to obtain true apex values for the subjects without prolonging the test unduly. Thus a total of 34 stimulus cards was presented to each subject and the threshold computed by the Summation Method (Woodworth, 1938, pp. 402-403).

22. *Speed of Perception (or Identification Threshold).* The stimulus material for this test was a series of black line drawings of familiar objects, such as cat, tree, bird, glasses, house, train, etc., presented in the tachistoscope. Since the dimensions of the drawings were approximately 1 x 1 in., they subtended a visual angle of about 2.4°. It was explained to the subject that a picture would appear in the exposure field for a brief moment, and that he was to try to name the picture as soon as possible. The initial exposure time for each picture was 15 ms, which interval was increased in steps of 5 ms until the object was identified. The total series consisted of 11 pictures, and the median of the identification thresholds constituted the score.

23. *Recognition Threshold for Non-meaningful Forms.* Black line drawings of non-meaningful forms were presented tachistoscopically at exposure intervals of .03 sec. After a practice run, a series of 24 cards was presented in standard order and after each presentation the subject was asked to select the correct form out of a group of four forms. In constructing the test forms, an attempt was made to develop a series of increasing difficulty. The total number of correct responses constituted the score.

24. *Azimuth Perception.*[4] Lines at angles of 18°, 36°, 54°, or 72° from the perpendicular, to the right or to the left, were presented, one at a time, in the tachistoscope for 2 sec. Following the presentation, the subject was asked to re-

[4] This test was designed by Dr. Noel S. Jenkin.

produce the position of the line on a grid. The grid had dotted lines for every 9 degrees. The series consisted of 16 trials in which each stimulus angle was presented twice.

For each response, the deviation from the stimulus angle was measured in degrees; deviations to the right indicated by a plus sign and to the left by a minus sign. If a response fell in the opposite quadrant, it was not scored in terms of angular deviation but as a reversal. Reversals were designated "R+" if the response was in the right quadrant and "R−" if it was in the left quadrant. Vertical responses were in no cases treated as reversals. The following scores were recorded: (a.) arithmetic mean deviation and (b.) total number of reversals.

25. *Brightness Discrimination.* The apparatus consisted of a wooden box, properly ventilated and divided into two sections by a thin plate of sheet metal, with a 40-watt incandescent lamp in each section. One of these lamps provided the light source for the reference part of the target and had a 100 ohm resistor inserted in the circuit. This provided the possibility of making the variable part of the target brighter, as well as dimmer, than the reference part. The variable light source was controlled by a General Radio Voltage Divider, Model 1454A. The target itself was an opal glass circle of 4 cm in diameter, covering an opening in the wooden box so the target was bisected by the sheet metal partition in the box. Thus there was a narrow dark dividing line between the reference and variable part of the target. The subject was seated 6 feet from the target, providing a visual angle of 1.2°. With the nondominant eye covered, the subject was asked to judge if the right half (the variable) was brighter or darker than the left half (the reference) at each step (.0002 on the voltage divider) of a series. Two ascending and two descending series were obtained. They were started with an ascending series where the variable part of the target was obviously darker.

In a manner similar to what has been described under Two-Point Threshold, an upper and lower value were determined for each series. The mean of these eight values was computed and transformed to millilamberts by means of a conversion table. From this value was substracted the brightness of the reference (43.9 ml) and this difference constituted the Brightness Error Score.

26. *Critical Flicker Fusion.* A Krasno-Ivy Flicker Photometer was used to determine critical flicker fusion (CFF). The instrument was modified so that discrete frequencies could be presented rather than continuously changing frequencies. The subject was seated 5 feet from the instrument, and the difference between steady and flickering light demonstrated. In a practice trial, a preliminary CFF threshold was established in an ascending and a descending series. The starting point for the test trials was 300 to 400 RPM (5 to 6.7 cps) from the preliminary threshold. Increasing or decreasing in steps of 50 RPM (0.83 cps), four series were conducted in alternating directions. For each frequency the subject had to judge whether the light was steady or flickering. A series was discontinued after two consecutive responses which were opposite to the response expected at the beginning of the series.

The mean of an upper and a lower transition point constituted a threshold, similarly to criterion for Two-Point Threshold and Brightness Discrimination. These values were transformed to cps, and the mean of the four trial thresholds constituted the score.

27. *Stereognosis.* It was reported desirable to include a test of Stereognosis in the battery, but the common procedure of having subjects reach into a bag to identify meaningful objects was rejected in favor of a non-verbal, objective (multiple choice) version with a controlled degree of difficulty established through pre-testing. The present arrangement represents a novel attempt to quantify this function. The test item consisted of a series of 27 wooden blocks of varying geometric forms which were placed in the subject's dominant hand, one at a time. The items were hidden from the subject's view by a partition placed over his arm. Simultaneously he was shown a circular board which had arranged on it a group of blocks containing the correct item, and instructed to point to the item which was the same as the one in his hand. The test was broken up into four groups, where one group consisted of six and three groups of seven stimulus blocks to be identified from a response group of 10 forms. The score was the total number of forms correctly identified.

28. *Time Interval Estimation.* The apparatus for this test consisted of a buzzer which could be activated by means of an interval timer or a telegraph key. Included in the circuit was a 1/100 sec. recording timer which was activated when the buzzer sounded. At each trial a demonstration period of 5 sec. was presented by the interval timer and the subject was asked to reproduce the interval by holding down the telegraph key for the same period of time (Clausen, 1950). After two practice trials a series of 20 test trials was administered and the median computed.

29. *Weight Lifting.* The purpose of this test was to obtain a measure for weight-size illusion. The test material (Whipple's modification of Gilbert's series) consisted of 2 standard weights and 20 comparison weights. The standards weighed 55 grams and were 28 mm high. The diameter of the largest standard was 82 mm and of the smaller standard 22 mm. The 20 comparison blocks were of uniform size, 28 mm high and 34 mm in diameter. Their weight ranged from 5 to 100 grams in steps of 5 grams.

The subject was instructed to lift the standard weight with the fingers of his dominant hand, then lift the comparison weight with the same hand and indicate which one was heavier or whether they were the same weight. The comparison weight was always on the side of the dominant hand. Throughout the series the standard was lifted before the comparison weight. The subject was asked to lift the weights in a certain rhythm as indicated by a metronome set at 70 beats per min. Sometimes the concept of heavier had to be explained or demonstrated more fully.

The procedure was again the psychophysical Method of Limits. Using the large standard, an ascending series of comparison weights was presented, starting with the 5 gram weight. The series was discontinued when reversed judgements were given to two successive trials. The second series was a descending one, starting with the 100 gram weight. The third (ascending) and fourth (descending) series were started four or five steps from the point of subjective equality shown in the first and second series. After a rest, the whole procedure was repeated with the small standard.

In the same way as has been described previously, thresholds were computed for each series, the mean for each standard determined, and the difference between them used as the measure of illusion.

30. *Muller-Lyer Illusion.* In preparing the apparatus for this test an attempt was made to amplify the illusion and to control the surroundings by constructing a large figure on a 48 x 60 in. board. One section of the figure was painted on the board, 21.5 in. from the top and 6.5 in. from the left edge. It could be partially occluded so that its length varied from 9 to 27 cm, by the movable section of the figure (20.5 cm long). The movement was achieved by a DC motor and an interval timer which controlled the current to the motor in such a fashion that the variation could be made in 0.5 cm steps. Thus the variable could be changed in discrete steps in either direction and the subject made his judgement of a stationary situation.

The subject was seated 8 feet from the apparatus. The nature of the task was explained to him, first by two pieces of cardboard, and then on the apparatus. After appropriate practice, three trials were conducted starting from extreme Out-Position. A trial was discontinued after two consecutive judgements which were opposite to the initial judgement of the series. In a similar manner, six trials were carried out starting from In-Position and three final trials from Out-Position. The score for extent of illusion was the Standard Value (20.5 cm) minus the mean for all 12 trials. Error of Anticipation was computed as the difference between the mean of the Out-Trials and the mean of the In-Trials.

31. *The Porteus Maze Test.* The test was administered and scored in accordance with the manual (Porteus, 1950). Scores for Mental Age and Test Quotient (IQ) were utilized.

32. *Raven's Matrices.* The complete test (Sets A, Ab, B, C, D, and E) was used. Instructions and scoring were in accordance with the manual (Raven, 1956) and the score was the total number of correct responses.

33. *Primary Mental Abilities.* It was regarded as essential for the purpose of the study to administer an intelligence test to the project population, and Thurstone's Test of Primary Mental Abilities was selected. The test was administered to small groups of six to eight subjects. At least two examiners took part in the administration to make sure that the nature of the task was understood by the child before proceeding with the actual test material.

Based on incidental information, age, existing IQ measures, general behavior, etc., it was estimated which form would be more appropriate for the individual child. Whenever the test results indicated that the situation was misjudged, the other form was administered. The test was administered in standard fashion according to the Examiner Manual (Thurstone, 1953, 1954). The range of the project population necessitated the use of both the 5 to 7 and 7 to 11 forms and since the factors involved in these forms are not identical, the scoring was limited to overall MA and IQ scores.

All of the foregoing tests were administered by standard instructions. In many cases these instructions had to be modified and supplemented until the subject had grasped the concept or nature of the task.

EVALUATION OF SUBJECT PERFORMANCE

The scoring sheet for each test contained a scale for rating the subject's attitude, behavior, and performance during the administration of the test. The scale is an adaptation of one described by King (1954), limited to an evaluation of the following five characteristics: Cooperation, Effort, Willingness, Attention, and Rapport. In accordance with King's procedure, a five point scale was used: No, Very Poor, Poor, Fair, and Good. In addition to these ratings, the examiner made an overall evaluation of his impression of how well the score expressed the subject's ability. A three category classification was used: No Confidence in the test result was indicated by 0, Questionable Confidence by 1, and High Confidence by 2. These ratings were considered in evaluating the reliability of observed group differences and reducing the *N* of groups when necessary.

ETIOLOGICAL CLASSIFICATION

Classification of etiology for the retarded population was made in accordance with the system described by Riggs and Rain (1952) and Riggs and Cassel (1952). By this system the retarded population was separated into groups of Familials, Organics, Unexplained, Mixed, Mongoloids, and Not Classifiable. From the records, essential information was transcribed to a work sheet designed by Riggs and Rain, and the individuals were classified in the prescribed manner. The Riggs and Rain system utilized medical, family, and developmental histories and the results of such specialized tests as neurological examination and EEG, in arriving at an estimate of etiological status.

NEUROLOGICAL EXAMINATION

All retarded children in the sample were given a standard neurological examination either during the testing period or shortly afterward. The examination included speech, apraxia and ataxia, gait and coordination, motor system, reflexes, sensations, and cranial nerve function. For each of these categories the findings were coded in the following way: Normal 0, Slight Impairment 1, Sever Impairment 2. An overall evaluation of neurological signs was attempted by totalling the separate evaluations—with Normal designated as the range from 0 to 2, Slight Impairment from 2 to 4, and Severe Impairment above 4. This gross differentiation of neurological categories is clearly arbitrary but seemed adequate for the present purposes.

In the present analysis, only the gross differentiation has been used, but the relationship between test performance and degree and type of impairment is discussed in a separate article (Clausen, in preparation)

The Normal control group in the present samples was not given a neurological examination, on the assumption that this group would be free of neurological symptoms. Observation of these children in the test situation did not contradict this assumption.

ELECTROENCEPHALOGRAPHIC RECORDING

During or shortly after the administration of the test battery, EEGs were recorded on all retarded subjects. Except for 14 cases, all tracings were recorded by the EEG technician of The Training School, and interpreted by Dr. Charles Henry. Throughout, attempt was made to obtain recordings in sleep as well as in the waking state but no sleep inducing agent was employed. Hyperventilation and stimulation by a Grass Photo Stimulator were used routinely.

In the earliest stage of the project the Photo Stimulator was not available, so photic stimulation was not used for the first 25 cases.. The EEGs were recorded on an 8-channel Grass Model III instrument, using 15 electrodes in a variety of monopolar and bipolar arrangements. Based on the interpretation of the records by the consultant, the findings were classified according to (a.) overall evaluation of degree of abnormality, (b.) type of abnormality, and (c.) locus of abnormality. The coding system for the degrees of abnormality was as follows: Normal pattern 0; Borderline pattern 1; Abnormal pattern only during sleep, hyperventilation, or photic stimulation 2; and Abnormal pattern in waking state 3.

Classification according to type and locus of abnormality produced subgroups which were too small to be utilized in the present analysis, but will be discussed in a separate report.

III POPULATION AND BACKGROUND VARIABLES

POPULATION

The original intent for the present study was to include 100 institutionalized retarded males in the age ranges of 8 to 10, 12 to 15, and 20 to 24, and a group of normal boys, chronological age 8 to 10. All retarded subjects were to be in the IQ range of 50 to 75, and the control group to have a mean of 100, as determined by the Chicago Test of Primary Mental Abilities. The three retarded samples were to be comparable in IQ (50 to 75) and etiological status and to be free from severe sensory, motor, or personality disturbance. The inclusion of a normal control sample in the CA range of 8 to 10 and mean IQ of 100 was for the purpose of being able to compare it with the youngest retarded group for CA and with the 12 to 15 year old sample for MA. As is often the case in a project of this size, it was impossible to realize all of the initial plans. In order to obtain as many subjects as desired for traditional factor analysis, it became necessary to include females. Even with this extension, however, it was impossible to obtain more than 68 subjects in the youngest retarded sample in the geographical area of the Ability Structure Project's (ASP) operation. Because of the difficulties which were encountered in administering the battery to the youngest retardates, those who were able to complete most of the tests tended to fall in a somewhat higher IQ range than the older retardates.

The normal subjects were obtained through the Public School System of Vineland. Contrary to original plans, the mean IQ of this group turned out to exceed 100, because of the markedly weaker response to ASP's recruiting efforts by the parents of children with IQs below 100.

The retarded children were drawn from institutions in South Jersey and East Pennsylvania. The institutions represented and the number of cases from each were as follows: The Training School at Vineland, N. J.–72 cases; Edward R. Johnstone Training and Research Center, Bordentown, N. J.–81 cases; State Colony at New Lisbon,

N. J.—57 cases; Vineland State School, Vineland, N. J.—26 cases; The Woods Schools, Langhorne, Pa.—16 cases; and Elwyn Training School, Elwyn, Pa.—24 cases.

The subjects from The Training School at Vineland, Vineland State School, and the normal subjects were tested in The Training School's laboratories. Subjects from outside Vineland were tested in their own institutions. All testing equipment, therefore, had to be moved to these locations which meant that the testing rooms and physical environment varied from one series of subjects to another, the consequences of which are difficult to evaluate. In any event, the reliabilities for the retarded samples compared favorably with those for the normal subjects who were tested under optimal conditions in The Training School's own laboratories. The children from Edward R. Johnstone Training and Research Center and the State Colony at New Lisbon were brought to Vineland for EEG. The children from the Woods Schools and from Elwyn Training School had EEGs in their respective institutions, in the latter situation, recorded by The Training School's technician.

Since the Ability Structure Project was primarily concerned with identifying subgroups on the basis of patterns of performance, it was deemed essential that as many subjects as possible be able to complete the entire battery. For this reason, individuals with severe motor and sensory defects and cases with gross personality disturbance were excluded from the retarded sample.

Several subjects had to be dropped from the project because of such factors as: speech problems, hearing difficulties, lack of cooperation, inability to understand instructions, or poor motor coordination. In many cases, these difficulties were not anticipated from information in the subject's institutional files. In other instances, however, where difficulties were suspected, especially in the youngest retarded sample, every attempt was made to obtain a complete set of test protocols.

Table 2 shows the number of subjects in the retarded and the normal samples. The youngest retarded sample (Sample 1) included 68 subjects, the 12-15 retardates (Sample 2) 105, the oldest retardates (Sample 3) 103, and the normals (Sample 4) 112 subjects. It can be seen that the ratio of males to females was 3:1 in the youngest retarded sample, 2:1 in the two older retarded samples, and approximately 1:1 in the normal sample. Frequency distribution of CA, MA, and IQ for the four samples (males and females combined) appears in Table 3. With regard to CA, it is seen that some of the subjects fell outside the intended age ranges, but the groups constituted separate

TABLE 2

NUMBER OF SUBJECTS IN THE FOUR SAMPLES

	Retardates 8–10	12–15	20–24	Normals 8–10	Total
Males	51	69	71	59	250
Females	17	36	32	53	138
Total	68	105	103	112	388

age distributions. The youngest retarded group was skewed toward the older side but the others represented relatively symmetrical distribution. As a result, the mean age for the 8-10 year old retardates was 7 months higher than for the normal control group. MA showed a fairly normal distribution for all four groups. Among the retardates, the 12-15 and 20-24 year old samples were fairly well matched. This suggests that there may not be any development of the functions measured by the PMA beyond the age range of 12-15. It is also worth noting that the normal subjects, on the average, had higher MA than the two older retarded samples. The intended MA matching between the 12-15 year old retardates and the normals was not accomplished, probably as a result of sampling problems and the academic nature of the PMA test. This problem will be more fully discussed later.

There seemed to be a tendency among the retarded samples toward a drop in IQ with increasing age. While the distribution within each group was reasonably symmetrical, a number of the retarded children fell below the cut-off point of 50 which had been originally set. This shift was in part due to the fact that in selecting subjects exceptions had to be made with regard to the lower limit, and in part to a general trend that the retarded subjects scored lower on this test than had been anticipated from the IQ data available in their files. This tendency to score lower on PMA could not be objectively verified because of the variety of tests cited in the files. The normal subjects had a mean IQ of about 112. This high mean was in part due to the selection of the control subjects. As it turned out, parents of the more intelligent children were more likely to permit them to take part in the program than were parents of children below 100. It is probable, too, that the test items of the PMA favor the children with a regular academic program.

TABLE 3

Chronological Age, Mental Age, and IQ Distribution

CA (in Months)	*Retarded 8–10*	*Retarded 12–15*	*Retarded 20–24*	*Norm 8–10*	*MA (in Months)*	*Retarded 8–10*	*Retarded 12–15*	*Retarded 20–24*	*Norm 8–10*
90–99	10			22	40–49	7			
100–109	12			44	50–59	16	8	6	
110–119	14			32	60–69	21	7	13	
120–129	30			14	70–79	13	21	23	
130–139	2	4			80–89	8	36	20	4
140–149		16			90–99	1	19	12	10
150–159		16			100–109	1	9	9	21
160–169		14			110–119		2	13	29
170–179		25			120–129		2	4	17
180–189		20			130–139		1	1	21
190–199		8			140–149			1	6
200–209		2			150–159				4
210–219									
220–229			1						
230–239			18						
240–249			19						
250–259			20						
260–269			17						
270–279			10						
280–289			11						
290–299			3						
300–309			2						
359			1						
390			1						
Mean CA	115	168	260	108	Mean MA	65	85	88	118

IQ Distribution

IQ	*Retarded 8–10*	*Retarded 12–15*	*Retarded 20–24*	*Normal 8–10*
20–29			1	
30–39	6	10	23	
40–49	11	26	38	
50–59	19	53	18	
60–69	24	12	20	
70–79	6	4	2	2
80–89	1			7
90–99				20
100–109				23
110–119				32
120–129				18
130–139				8
140–149				2
Mean IQ	57	52	49	110

The frequency distribution for each retarded sample is entered in Table 4 for the etiological, neurological, and EEG categories used in the present study. Regarding etiological classification, the three age samples presented essentially the same picture: the organics as the dominant group and relatively few familials. The sizable number of subjects who showed evidence of both familial and organic etiology is of interest. Also worth noting is the fact that the Unknown and the Not Classifiable constituted about 20% of the sample.

TABLE 4

FREQUENCIES OF ETIOLOGICAL, NEUROLOGICAL, AND EEG CATEGORIES FOR EACH OF THE RETARDED SAMPLES

Etiological Classification	*8–10*	*12–15*	*20–24*	*Total*
Familials	10	14	8	32
Organics	38	42	43	123
Mixed	11	27	12	50
Unknown	6	10	20	36
Not Classifiable	3	8	12	23
Mongoloid	0	4	8	12
TOTAL	68	105	103	276
Overall Neurological Signs				
Normal	43	74	52	169
Slight Impairment	20	23	30	73
Severe Impairment	3	7	15	25
Not available for examination	2	1	6	9
TOTAL	68	105	103	276
Degree of EEG Abnormality				
Normal	19	27	43	89
Borderline	15	32	28	75
Abnormal Pattern only in sleep, hyperventilation, or photic stimulation	4	7	4	15
Abnormal	29	34	20	83
EEG not available	1	5	8	14
TOTAL	68	105	103	276

The striking thing in the distribution of Overall Neurological Signs is that only 25 children out of 276, or 10%, were classified as Severely Impaired, in the way this term has been defined above. While the initial selection screened out some children who were severely impaired (severe motor and sensory disturbance), the fact remains that almost 70% of the retarded sample did not show positive neurological signs. This may be contrasted with the frequencies in the various EEG categories, which suggests greater sensitivity in the EEG examination in differentiating subjects.

TESTING SCHEDULE

All subjects were seen twice a week during the testing period. The test sessions for the older retardates and the normals lasted for about one hour, which made it possible to finish the total test program in eight sessions. The test sessions for the younger and lower grade retardates were shorter, lasting from 30 to 50 min., thus necessitating 11 sessions or more. In addition to these sessions, came the neurological examination and the recording of EEG.

The data were collected over a period of three years, from January 1958 to December 1960. All tests, except the PMA, were administered individually. At any time, groups of from 10 to 37 subjects were included, depending upon the number of examiners and number of subjects available. There were generally three or four examiners available. The order of presentation of tests varied to a certain extent from subject to subject. A rotating schedule was arranged so that each child was seen by all examiners and each examiner administered a different portion of the battery to successive groups. The number and selection of tests for a given session were determined by duration of administration time and task difficulties.

While a certain degree of flexibility was necessary with respect to the order in which the tests were administered, some tests had a fixed position in the battery. Lateral dominance was always determined before the tests which required the use of the preferred hand; simple auditory reaction time was administered before auditory choice reaction time; and, in almost all cases, the PMA was administered in group form as the last test of the battery.

It is our impression that the extent of the present program in terms of testing time was close to the limit of what can safely be used, particularly for the youngest retarded sample.

From a practical point of view it was desirable to have complete data for all subjects. For a variety of reasons this was not always possible: some children were discharged from the institution or transferred to another institution during the testing program; illness occurred; or a subject refused to do a particular task. Missing scores occurred most frequently in the youngest retarded sample, the mean being 2.0 per measure. The means for the two older retarded samples and the normal sample were all less than 1.0. The tests which contributed a large portion of the missing data were Orthorater, Mirror Drawing, and Muller-Lyer. The missing data were replaced by the medians of the respective distributions. A total of 168 scores have been added to 19788, which is less than 1%.

IV RESULTS

SAMPLE COMPARISONS

SEX COMPARISONS

The first problem to be considered was whether the combining of male and female subjects was permissible. As can be seen from Table 2, the number of girls in the youngest retarded sample was not sufficient to warrant separate treatment. Also, the combining of boys and girls would increase the *N* in each sample or comparison group, thus strengthening the conclusions that might be drawn from the data.

Sex comparisons were made separately for each of the four samples. The statistical procedure was first to determine the homogeneity of variance for each variable by computing the variance ratio for the two sexes. If this ratio did not reach the 5% level of significance, variances were pooled and the regular *t* test used to determine difference between means. If the variance ratio was significant, variances were not pooled in determining the difference between the means. Since *t* tests were computed for sex difference in all fifty variables in the four samples, some significant differences could have occurred by chance alone. Also, it may have happened, particularly in the retarded samples, that the two sex groups were not matched for a variety of dimensions such as etiology, organic involvement, etc., and that what appeared to be sex differences actually reflected entirely different factors. On such considerations, the criterion was adopted that a difference should occur in the normal sample and be substantiated in one or more of the retarded samples in order to be regarded as a genuine sex difference. A possible objection to this criterion would be that the normal sample was younger than two of the retarded samples and that some of the sex differences may not have developed fully in the 10 year old normals. There are some indications in the data that this was the case. There were 4 significant differences in Sample 1, 15 in Sample 2, and 12 in Sample 3. This may represent a trend, but the evidence is far from conclusive. The fact that 7 differences occurred in the normal sample, which was slightly younger than the youngest retarded sample, does not support the existence of a relationship.

Also, the limited number of significant differences in the youngest retarded sample may have been a result of the few girls in this group.

While it may seem reasonable to believe that sex differences become more pronounced with increasing age, it is possible that such development may be related to IQ level or performance level as well as to the factor of chronological age. These problems can only be answered by comparing sex differences for normals and retardates at various age levels. Under present circumstances, the criterion adopted for sex differences seems the most adequate. The variables which satisfy this criterion are entered in Table 5. The table shows that only five variables—out of the 50—indicated sex differences, Grip L & R, Tapping, Mirror Drawing Total Time, Azimuth Arithmetic, and CFF. To illustrate the sex differences in the four samples, the means of the males and females, expressed as *T* scores with reference to the mean and standard deviation of the total normal sample, are presented in Fig. 2.

TABLE 5

LEVEL OF SIGNIFICANCE WHEN SEX-DIFFERENCES OCCUR IN THE NORMAL AND RETARDED SAMPLES

Variable	*8–10*	*12–15*	*20–24*	*Normal*
Grip L	5%	5%	1%	1%
Grip R		5%	1%	1%
Tapping			5%	5%
Mirr. Dr. T.T.			1%	5%
Azimuth, Arith.		5%		5%
CFF	5%	1%		1%

The *T* scores have been computed by the formula $T=\frac{(X\text{-}Mn)}{\sigma} 10 + 50$, where Mn is the mean and σ is the standard deviation of the total normal sample (N=112). This makes the mean of the total normal sample 50 and the standard deviation 10. Thus the means for all variables in the total normal sample are represented by a straight line through 50. The purpose of this transformation was to have all measures on a comparable scale. The general impression from Fig. 2 is that the sex differences were minor and generally inconsistent. By inspecting the means it was found that Tapping scores showed significant difference in the 20-24 retarded and in the normal sample, with better performance by the girls. The 12-15 retarded sample showed a trend in the opposite direction, which cast some doubt on the validity of the sex difference explanation. The remaining four variables showed higher scores for boys than for girls in all four samples with two or more of them significant.

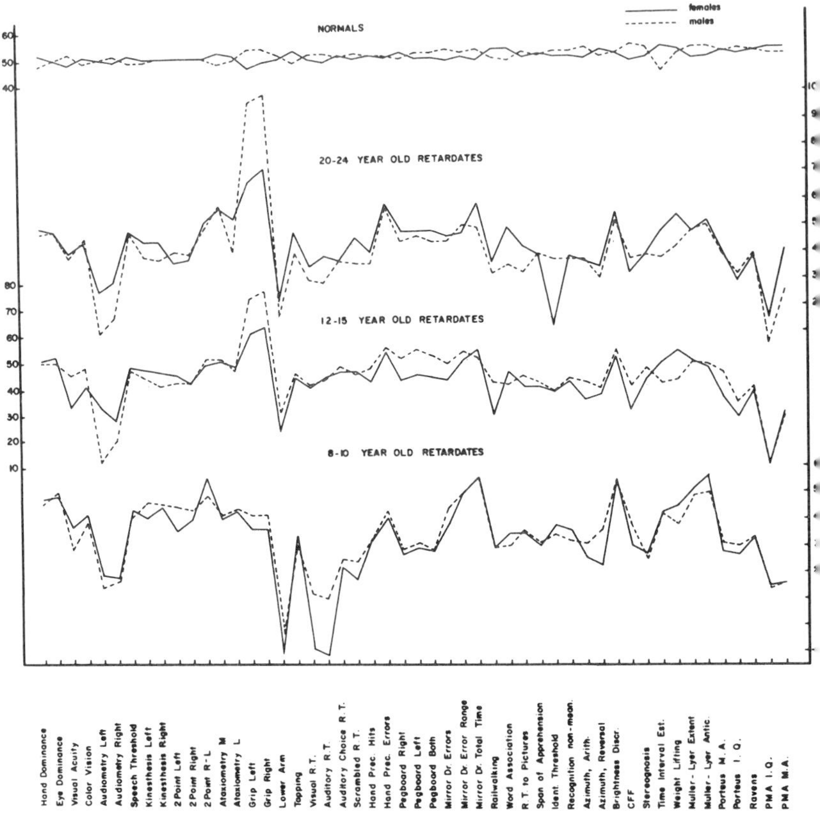

Figure 2. *T* scores plotted separately for males and females of the four samples.

It was certainly not surprising to find that boys had a stronger grip than girls (e.g., Whipple, 1914; Baldwin, 1921; Meredith, 1935; Jones, 1949). Sex differences have previously been reported for CFF (Miller, 1942). Sex differences in the ability to reproduce the angular position of a line (Azimuth) does not seem to have been reported before. The possibly superior performance by the girls in Tapping was unexpected, since it is generally accepted that in the motor task area boys surpass girls. In line with this, one might have expected better performance by the boys, and also significant differences in perceptual and complex variables, with the girls having superior scores (e.g. Mussen & Conger, 1956, p. 179).

It should be kept in mind for the subsequent discussion of developmental trends that Fig. 2 indicates a reversal of male-female performance level from Sample 2 to Sample 3, especially for motor tasks

In addition to analysis of single variables, the Mean *T* score and the *SD* for each individual around his own *T* score mean (across-trait variability) were considered. Excluded from this analysis were Grip Right and Left, since these were such deviant scores, and CA, which left 48 variables. The group means of these two measures for males and females separately are entered in Table 9. In the youngest retarded sample the boys had a slightly higher Mean *T* than the girls, with the trend reversed in the oldest retarded sample, although the differences between boys and girls were not significant. The oldest boys had a lower Mean *T* than the 12-15 year old boys, while the oldest girls had a higher score than the 12-15 year old girls. The indication of differential developmental trends in boys and girls in the sample may have been a result of sampling. *SD* of *T* showed the same trend: no difference between boys and girls in the normal and oldest retarded samples and a slight trend to higher *SD* of *T* among the boys than the girls in the two youngest retarded samples.

The slight and inconsistent sex differences in these data indicated that pooling of boys and girls in subsequent group comparisons was justified.

GENERAL DESCRIPTION OF ABILITY PROFILE

Through a general discussion of Ability Profiles some insight may be gained about the patterns of abilities of retarded subjects with reference to the normal control sample. The descriptive statistics for the four samples are presented in Table 6 together with a short descriptive title and the unit of measurement. For further details about the scores and unit of measurement, see Table 1 and previous description of test procedures. The differences between the four samples, are illustrated in Fig. 3, where the sample means for all variables are expressed as *T* scores in terms of the mean and standard deviation of the normal sample. The direction of excellency in this figure has been made uniform by reversing some of the scores, so that a high *T* score means a good performance in accordance with entries in Table 1. For some of the variables it was difficult to decide what the direction of excellency was. This was particularly true with Weight Lifting, Muller-Lyer Extent, and Muller-Lyer Anticipation, where the scores reflected degree of illusion. In keeping with standard practice, a high degree of illusion was regarded as the preferred performance.

The sequence of the variables in Table 6 and Fig. 3 is the same as described before, namely four domains of functions, sensory, motor, perceptual, and complex mental functions with increasing degree of

TABLE 6

Means and Standard Deviations for the Four Samples

Variable	*Unit*	*8–10 Ret.* *M*	*S.D.*	*12–15 Ret.* *M*	*S.D.*	*20–24 Ret.* *M*	*S.D.*	*Normals* *M*	*S.D.*
Hand. Dom.	code	2.62	0.90	3.14	0.94	3.02	1.12	3.09	1.20
Eye Dom.	code	2.32	1.71	2.33	1.71	2.27	1.65	2.24	1.75
Vis. Acuity	code	5.26	2.24	7.37	2.25	7.05	2.57	8.52	1.50
Color Vis.	score	2.07	1.19	2.60	1.09	2.66	1.20	2.97	0.87
Audio. L	code	22.91	18.46	21.08	17.79	22.83	19.61	5.54	5.07
Audio. R	code	23.74	21.61	19.88	17.99	20.96	19.61	4.42	5.72
Speech Thres.	db	58.04	10.08	62.56	7.29	62.45	8.82	63.73	6.83
Kinesth. L	cm	0.34	0.20	0.36	0.23	0.41	0.22	0.26	0.20
Kinesth. R	cm	0.33	0.19	0.39	0.21	0.40	0.21	0.26	0.17
2-Point L	mm	21.41	11.62	21.72	11.07	23.55	9.23	15.33	8.74
2-Point R	mm	21.83	10.19	22.39	10.38	23.80	8.90	16.45	7.64
2-Point R-L	mm	0.37	7.08	0.58	7.53	0.21	7.51	1.03	6.45
Atax. M	code	1.74	0.24	1.58	0.25	1.46	0.25	1.61	0.16
Atax. L	code	1.60	0.33	1.47	0.31	1.43	0.31	1.41	0.33
Grip L	kg.	9.48	3.70	20.60	7.99	28.00	10.42	13.10	3.84
Grip R	kg.	10.64	4.09	22.56	8.40	30.19	10.46	14.17	3.78
Lower Arm	ms	524	279	347	145	400	184	233	53
Tapping	no.	7.58	2.06	9.58	2.46	9.39	2.88	10.37	1.45
Vis. RT	ms	454	198	292	137	331	167	249	47
Audio. RT	ms	387	200	241	112	280	150	217	37
Aud. Choice RT	ms	732	260	513	202	603	415	487	96
Scrambled RT	ms	566	197	388	188	426	180	352	77
Hand Prec. Hits	no.	35.86	8.01	41.47	4.23	38.35	7.98	43.46	4.41
Hand Prec. Err.	no.	8.80	3.55	5.60	3.38	4.30	3.71	6.70	2.67
Pegboard R	# of pegs	27.82	6.99	38.24	8.43	37.02	8.59	39.04	5.15
Pegboard L	# of pegs	27.24	7.30	37.10	7.90	36.01	8.78	36.76	4.79
Pegboard B	# of pegs	20.49	6.43	29.76	7.04	28.26	8.04	30.05	4.32
Mirr. Dr. Err.	no.	87.90	24.68	73.36	45.45	78.01	59.66	62.16	35.83
Mirr. Dr. Err. Ra.	no.	63.20	49.33	52.93	48.23	61.19	52.33	62.06	42.43
Mirr. Dr. T. T.	sec.	60.07	23.08	71.08	32.50	68.10	33.93	75.29	24.66
Railwalking	%tot.dist.	36.74	22.25	50.04	25.79	45.27	23.65	69.49	15.61
Word Assoc.	ms	3330	1067	2560	957	2732	1004	2107	664
Percep. Speed	ms	1146	264	1024	269	1136	380	889	179
Span of Appre.	# of dots	3.67	1.33	4.76	1.22	4.54	1.09	5.55	0.99
Ident. Thres.	ms	70.56	59.81	66.22	75.82	78.77	104.03	48.29	15.29
Recogn.	correct	8.54	2.60	11.20	3.29	9.92	3.18	13.37	2.85
Azimuth, Arith.	degrees	1.29	0.21	1.12	0.19	1.15	0.19	0.94	0.17
Azimuth, Rev.	no.	3.03	2.61	2.32	2.52	3.16	3.21	0.75	1.36
Brightn. Discr.	mL	0.71	4.90	1.44	4.27	1.34	6.39	2.68	4.29
CFF	cps	37.30	3.18	37.47	3.52	37.18	3.91	40.92	2.63
Stereogn.	score	15.72	4.73	20.17	3.72	18.88	4.04	21.29	2.29
Time Int. Est.	1/100 sec.	484	213	478	174	498	157	436	69
Weight Lift.	gram	23.80	16.96	30.14	13.06	30.38	17.47	34.45	10.14
Muller-L. Ext.	cm	5.10	1.54	4.92	1.57	4.95	1.64	5.21	1.37
Muller-L. Antic.	cm	1.63	2.54	2.34	3.17	1.61	2.57	1.84	1.56
Porteus M.A.	year	5.45	1.81	8.19	3.06	7.94	2.84	10.17	2.43
Porteus I.Q.	—	56.99	17.60	62.73	23.00	56.61	20.08	111.94	26.64
Raven	score	13.68	5.18	20.97	7.94	20.10	7.87	33.01	11.41
PMA-M.A.	months	65	12	85	15	88	20	118	16
PMA-I.Q.	—	57.28	10.57	51.85	8.90	48.56	11.05	109.55	14.78
C.A.	months	115	12	168	17	260	24	108	9

complexity within the domains. Such grouping has practical advantages in the discussion of the findings—when so many variables are involved, even though the precise definition of the categories constitutes a problem, and the designation of the variables into the several categories may give rise to some arguments.

Fig. 3 indicates a considerable similarity in the curve profiles described by the three retarded samples. While the levels for many variables may differ substantially, there was a general tendency for the direction of change from one variable to the next to be uniform in the three samples. Most of the sensory variables were relatively

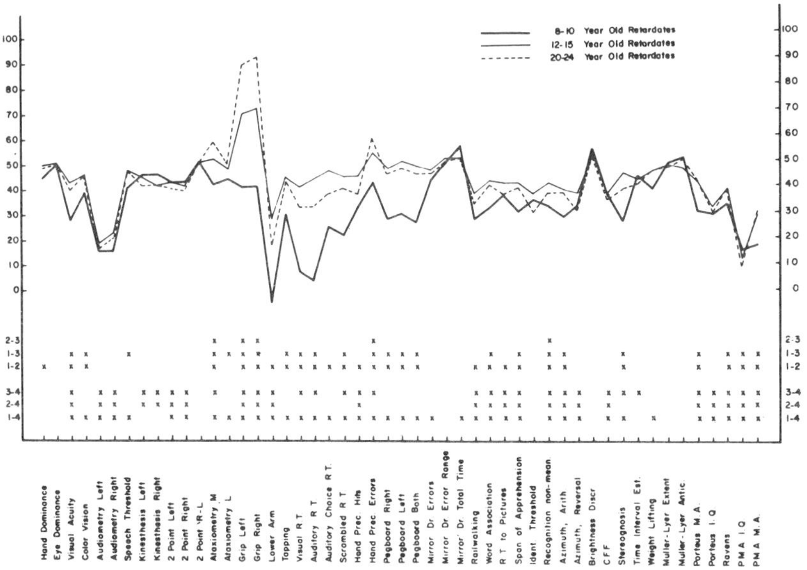

Figure. 3. Group means for the four samples plotted in terms of mean and standard deviation for the normals (T scores). The means for the normals fall all on the 50 mark. The x marks indicate differences between the various samples which reach the 1% level of significance.

close to the normal value, with the notable exception of the two Audiometry measures and perhaps also Visual Acuity. Of the motor measures, Grip tended to be high while the others had a tendency to increase in level with increasing complexity. The marked pattern of low score for Lower Arm, higher score for Tapping, and a drop in score for Visual RT was found in all three samples. The perceptual measures had all relatively low scores, with little difference between variables and little difference between samples. These measures showed less consistency of pattern than was found in any of the other domains. The complex variables showed marked pattern consistency; the level was low—lower for the two PMA variables than for the Raven and Porteus variables. The variables are discussed in further detail below.

The uniformity of the profiles of the three retarded samples would indicate the existence of a general "Ability Structure" for the mentally retarded, unless it can be shown that subsamples of retardates—e.g., etiological categories—have distinctly different profiles. For the total samples presented in Fig. 3 Kendall's coefficient of concordance indicates highly significant concordance (Chi Square equals 1234 with .001 level of significance being 86.7). Since perceptual measures seemed to have less consistency in pattern than variables from the other domains, Kendall's coefficient of concordance was computed for perceptual measures alone, and found to be significant at the .01 level.

With some exceptions, there was a general tendency for the means of all three retarded samples to fall below the mean of the normals. This shows that there were a number of variables where the adult retardates did not reach the performance level of the normal 8-10 year olds.

While the youngest retarded sample in general showed the poorest performance, there was a tendency for the 20-24 year old retardates to fall below the 12-15 year olds. Instead of a gradual increase of performance with age, a decline seemed to develop between the ages of 15 and 20. This trend occurred somewhat more often for the boys (26 times) than the girls (19 times). This sex difference was particularly found in some manipulative motor variables, Hand Precision and Pegboard, where the oldest retarded girls had better scores than the 12-15 retarded girls, while this was reversed for the corresponding age-sample of boys. The reason for the reversal of trend in the oldest retardates is obscure. It may be a general tendency that is also found in the general population, although existing evidence does not support this. (See the Review of the Respective Variables elsewhere in this chapter). It has been suggested that life in institutions provides less stimulation and more limited range of experience than does family life and could therefore be the cause of deterioration of performance as adolescence is reached. With the active programs in most of the institutions from which the present sample was drawn, this does not seem a likely explanation. It is more reasonable to believe that the poorer performance of the oldest retardates was a result of selective factors: it is the individual with the generally poorest performance who remains in the institutions beyond the age of 20. Further information on this problem would be relatively easy to obtain by conducting a follow-up study on the 12-15 year old sample about 5-6 years after the original testing. Repeated testing with selected tests from the battery should determine whether these individuals have gained, maintained the same level, or deteriorated in comparison with the original testing. From such a study it could also be ascertained whether continued institutionalization or discharge is related to the type of performance level that is recorded by these tests.

Audiometry scores for both left and right ear showed considerable deficiency in all three retarded samples, while Threshold for Speech was much closer to the normal level. It may be remembered that the Audiometry score was a composite of frequencies in the speech range.

This discrepancy can therefore hardly be ascribed to functional defects of the auditory apparatus in the retardates. It seems more likely that it is related to attentional or motivational factors. It may be easier to attend to a spoken word which conveys a meaning than to the "abstract" pure tone of the audiometer. The discrepancy between these two tests appears to cast grave doubt on audiometric testing as an appropriate method of assessing hearing functions in the retardates (see also Schlanger, 1961). One should, however, be cautious about rejecting audiometric testing, as just this difference may be of profound interest for understanding the nature of these individuals' communication problems.

The variables in which the two older retarded samples were unquestionably superior to the reference sample were Strength of Grip for left and right hand while the youngest retardates fell below the normals of comparable age range. The age norms given in the literature for 12-15 and 20-24 year old normals (Whipple, 1914; Baldwin, 1921; Metheny, 1941; Jones, 1949), however, show that this was also the case for the older retarded samples. While the comparisons here were complicated by the fact that Strength of Grip was the test where sex difference was most clearly pronounced, and that the male-female ratio in the four samples was not identical, this test showed the clearest progression through the entire age range of retardates. Thus it appeared that this test, better than any other, reflected physical growth of the individuals.

Among the lowest scores in all three retarded samples was Lower Arm Movement. This was surprising since it had been designed as a particularly simple motor task, and it was expected that the retardates would deviate from the normals more for the complex than for the simple tasks. As we have mentioned above, the motor scores in Fig. 3 are arranged in accordance with what was believed to be increasing degree of complexity, starting with Ataxiometry and culminating with Railwalking. Strength of Grip showed some unique characteristics which were not shared by any of the other measures in that it was so closely related to chronological age. If this particular test be disregarded, it is seen in the figure that with increase of complexity in the motor variables there was a general tendency to an increase in *T* score and to a closer approximation to the performance of the control sample. The similarity of these tendencies in the three independent samples of retardates gave considerable weight to this trend.

Similarly to Strength of Grip, Railwalking did not seem to fit into the general pattern of impairment's being related to the complexity of the task. Railwalking requires coordination of many different muscle groups as well as visual cues, and must therefore be considered a complex task. Nevertheless, Railwalking was one of the most impaired variables among the motor tasks, particularly for the two older retarded groups. It was also seen that Railwalking showed less developmental gain than did most motor tasks. Apparently then, the relationship between impairment and task complexity was limited to manipulative and speed tasks. It is possible that the impairment of integration of visual cues and gross motor movement was responsible for the low performance level on the Railwalking task.

It is not easy, at this stage, to interpret the findings of relationship between deficiency and task complexity among the manipulative and speed tasks. Lower Arm Movement is a speed measure; it requires very little muscular coordination, does not require attention to a starting signal, but depends heavily on voluntary initiation of response. The opinion may be offered that more than anything else a good score depends upon effort or drive, the ambition to do one's very best. This may also be the case with the simple RTs where performance level was also low. In contrast, Tapping Test showed relatively high group means, where response initiation was eliminated by the test procedure.

It appears from Fig. 3 that the improvement with age was greater for the motor variables than for the perceptual variables. The general picture for the motor variables was that the youngest retarded sample performed considerably below the reference group. The 12-15 sample showed substantial improvement, in that they were performing at or close to the level of the controls, while the oldest retarded sample had deteriorated noticeably for these variables. For the perceptual measures, the youngest retardates were not nearly as much below the normals as they were for the motor tasks. The 12-15 year old retardates showed poorer performance for perceptual than for motor tasks. They showed improvement over the youngest retarded sample for perceptual measures but not nearly as much as they had shown for motor tasks. The oldest retardates were below the performance level of the 12-15 year olds for perceptual variables. They performed on the same level as they did for simple motor tasks, but below their level for complex motor tasks. Thus there was a smaller increment with age for the perceptual measures, so that with initially smaller deficiency all retarded samples remained below the performance level of the 8-10 year old normal sample.

This supports a finding reported by Tizard, O'Connor, and Crawford (1950). They administered the US Employment Service General Aptitude Test Battery to 104 high-grade adult retardates and found the median score of Spatial Aptitude to be 1 *SD* below normal, Form Perception and Aiming or Hand Coordination 1½ *SD*, Finger and Manual Dexterity 2 *SD*, and Motor Speed 2½ *SD* below normal. Although hesitantly, Tizard concluded: "It would seem from this evidence that the mentally defective subjects had higher median scores on the more abstract tests of Spatial Aptitude and Form Perception than on the tests demanding precision of movements, manual and finger dexterity, and especially, motor speed."

As will be seen in subsequent discussion of the data, two variables had a marked tendency to show deviant trends as compared with the other motor measures, namely Hand Precision Errors and Mirror Drawing Total Time. In Fig. 3 it may be seen that they were among the few tasks where the older retardates had a tendency to perform better than the normals. Both of these measures derived from tests where several scores had been obtained to evaluate the level of performance. These different scores are not independent; one may gain speed at the expense of accuracy and vice versa. Combination of such scores is a long standing problem because of the difference in measuring unit, but should be simplified with the conversion to *T* scores. It may be suggested that while general level of these variables reflects motor efficiency, relations between error and time reflect attitude toward or manner of solving a problem. For Hand Precision, if one does not try to move the stylus every time a target is exposed, there will be fewer hits, which is detrimental, but also affords a reduction of errors. Similarly with Mirror Drawing, one may make good timing at the expense of number of errors, or vice versa. By averaging two *T* scores for Hand Precision, the following scores were obtained: 38, 49, and 46 for the three retarded samples respectively, and by averaging the *T* scores for Mirror Drawing Error and Total Time, 52, 52, and 52 were found for the three samples. Obviously the greater speed in Mirror Drawing was not all gained at the expense of more errors. It may have been due to less interference from previously established eye-hand coordination, which interference may have depressed the scores of the normals. In light of these considerations it was only the combined score for Hand Precision in the youngest retarded sample that showed a substantial deviation from the control sample. The Mirror Drawing scores for the retardates were less influenced by task attitude, and the lack of interference from previously established hand-eye coordination compensated for the impaired motor coordination, which resulted in a performance level as good as that of the normals.

For the complex mental functions the two oldest retarded samples, as would be expected, had MA scores which were closer to the normal sample than were the age-related IQs. Porteus and Raven resulted in higher performance level than PMA, thus supporting the expectation that the retardates would perform relatively better on those tasks which were not as closely related to academic skills as were the PMA tasks. The PMA-MA had particularly low performance level. The 20-24 year old retardates had three variables with lower performance level than PMA-MA, the 12-15 sample had two, and the 8-10 sample had five. Thus it was indicated that the integrative mechanism of complex mental functioning is a primary manifestation of retardation, and that the composite intelligence measures remain one of the most significant diagnostic procedures for the retarded segment of the population.

Further details in the comparison of the four samples will be discussed when we turn our attention to other aspects of the statistical analysis of the data.

Discussion

The inspection of the Ability Structure Profiles has indicated that the three retarded samples differed in characteristic ways from a normal sample as well as from each other. While there were sufficient similarities in the profiles of the three retarded samples to indicate a "retardate ability structure," differences in patterns within domains were also clearly indicated. The domains of sensory and complex functions showed similarities in levels as well as in patterns. The domain of motor functions showed general similarity in patterns but pronounced differences in levels, while the perceptual functions showed relatively small differences in levels and less consistency in patterns than was found in the other domains. Thus it was strongly indicated that rate of development and maturation age differ for the various functions. Further details about development patterns will be presented below.

For the great majority of the functions, the retarded samples—including the 20-24 year olds—performed on an inferior level as compared to the 8-10 year old normals. This indicates that we were dealing with a "deficient" condition rather than a "retarded" one, since the latter phrase implies slower progress but the ultimate attainment of normal proficiency. The deficiency, however, was not uniform for all tasks. The impairment showed up particularly in Audiometric measures, Lower Arm Movement, the four RT measures, Railwalking, all perceptual measures except Brightness Discrimination and those involving illusions, and complex mental functions, particularly PMA. In contrast to this, most sensory functions, some complex motor functions—Hand Precision and Mirror Drawings—and the perceptual variables—Brightness Discrimination, Weight Lifting, and Muller-Lyer—were relatively intact. While it is difficult to explain adequately all details in these patterns, the poor performance on several tasks resulted from impairment of a number of functions: attentional, motivational, or alertness factors in Audiometry; response initiation and effort or drive in Lower Arm Movement; attention and effort in the RT measures; integration of gross motor movements and visual cues in Railwalking; and factors of integration in perceptual and complex mental variables. Measures such as Mirror Drawing, Weight Lifting, and Muller-Lyer may have been adequately performed by the retardates because their contact with the outside world had not established sufficiently firm patterns to interfere with the performance of these tasks, as was the case in the normals.

COMPARISON OF RETARDATES TO NORMALS

For each of the fifty variables an analysis of variance between the four samples (simple randomized design) was conducted. The *F*s for the fifty variables are listed in Column I of Table 7. In a few cases the resulting *F* ratio did not reach the 5% level of significance, which indicates that for these variables the retarded samples did not differ from the normals or from each other. The variables were Eye Dominance, Two-Point Difference, Mirror Drawing Error Range, Brightness Error, Muller-Lyer Extent, and Muller-Lyer Anticipation. The six variables may readily be identified in Fig. 3 as those measures where the means of all three retarded samples are close to 50. Identification Threshold barely reached the 5% level for *F*, but none of the comparisons for paired samples reached the 1% level by *t* test. Thus laterality as indicated by Eye Dominance in these retardates was not different from that of normals. No differentiation for Two-Point Difference, in face of significant difference for Two-Point Threshold on both right and left side of the body, showed that the retardates had a tendency to a bilateral discrimination deficiency. Discrimination deficiency caused by localized cortical impairment would most often be a unilateral manifestation. The bilateral manifestation may therefore indicate that the deficiency was a result of impairment of general factors such as alertness, attention, or motivation, rather than specific cortical damage. Mirror Drawing Error Range indicated that the

TABLE 7

F-RATIO FROM OVERALL ANALYSIS OF VARIANCE FOR EACH VARIABLE WITHIN THE TOTAL SAMPLE AND VARIOUS SUBSAMPLES

Test	*Total Sample DF 3/384*	*Developm. Sample 2/117*	*Neuro. Sample 2/72*	*EEG Sample 2/225*	*Neuro. & EEG Sample 3/152*	*Etiol. Sample 3/124*
Hand Dom.	3.79	2.26	1.73	.53	.59	2.62
Eye Dom.	.06	.43	4.57	1.30	1.28	.99
Vis. Acuity	32.31	14.07	1.85	.84	2.08	.03
Color Vis.	9.71	7.09	.03	.59	.89	.15
Audio. L	28.85	.01	1.67	.60	.10	2.43
Audio. R	27.17	1.58	1.38	.15	.24	1.63
Speech Thresh.	7.24	8.82	.17	.48	.76	.12
Kinesth. R	11.50	5.40	.19	.03	1.23	.26
Kinesth. L	9.30	1.18	.35	.27	.72	.21
2-Point L	13.48	.88	.09	1.59	.09	.85
2-Point R	13.06	.89	.57	.73	.10	1.60
2-Point R-L	.25	.15	.86	.50	.05	.70
Atax. M	21.53	10.70	1.17	2.01	1.61	1.15
Atax. L	5.68	2.20	3.84	.26	.54	1.64
Grip L	116.04	68.02	4.28	6.36	3.95	1.06
Grip R	126.22	76.03	1.92	8.48	6.09	1.54
Lower Arm	43.41	15.39	3.48	5.74	2.71	.92
Tapping	21.25	18.99	2.95	3.33	3.45	.79
Vis. R. T.	30.89	10.25	2.80	4.98	5.01	.91
Audio. R. T.	26.51	13.76	1.90	4.65	2.44	.40
Aud. Choice R.T.	13.91	16.37	2.62	6.47	4.48	.84
Scrambl. R.T.	25.60	15.31	1.01	6.27	3.07	.88
Hand Prec. Hits	25.57	2.57	5.63	1.95	3.77	1.83
Hand Prec. Err.	26.76	21.13	2.30	4.55	3.87	.33
Pegboard R	37.03	33.22	6.63	4.23	6.87	.55
Pegboard L	31.01	29.83	9.37	2.36	6.54	.42
Pegboard B	35.38	26.87	9.42	5.21	8.98	.77
Mirr. Dr. Err.	5.08	10.13	.03	4.46	2.64	.87
Mirr. Dr. Err. Ra.	.93	4.21	.30	2.72	.56	1.75
Mirr. Dr. T.T.	3.94	3.12	.86	.51	.80	.14
Railwalking	37.49	4.60	10.91	9.98	14.19	2.60
Word Assoc.	25.59	9.33	1.29	1.88	.00	.44
Percep. Speed	17.80	2.73	.71	2.18	1.88	.24
Span of Appre.	39.30	6.01	1.50	3.36	2.82	.29
Ident. Thres.	3.42	1.78	.25	.46	1.81	.19
Recogn.	42.03	14.22	3.23	2.93	2.52	.74
Azimuth. Arith.	53.88	9.31	1.53	1.69	.93	.08
Azimuth. Rev.	20.19	.45	.33	.52	1.03	.45
Brightness Discr.	2.53	.07	.05	1.19	.41	.23
CFF	30.49	.43	.48	1.32	2.23	2.91
Stereogn.	34.38	15.92	2.35	1.14	1.78	.09
Time Int. Est.	3.18	.27	.42	2.19	.11	.29
Weight Lift.	7.65	8.78	.63	.24	.87	1.10
Muller-L. Ext.	.78	.10	.21	.36	.49	.67
Muller-L. Antic.	1.79	1.17	.83	.51	1.77	1.29
Porteus M.A.	45.30	19.71	.38	9.11	4.21	1.17
Poretus I.Q.	145.93	2.40	.52	6.64	3.18	1.15
Raven	80.23	16.34	.59	2.62	.52	.27
PMA-M.A.	162.77	41.61	.17	1.59	1.35	.24
PMA-I.Q.	646.45	2.28	.02	.07	.63	.97
CA	1,734.81	674.66	.06	2.99	.14	.13
5% level	2.62	3.07	3.13	3.04	2.67	2.68
1% level	3.83	4.79	4.92	4.71	3.91	3.94
1% level	5.70	7.31	7.70	7.20	5.79	5.79

normals were not reducing the number of errors throughout the series any faster than were the retardates. At their level of performance, the retardates improved their scores at the same rate as the normals. As mentioned above this may be related to the firmness with which eye-hand coordination was established. It was puzzling to find that the retarded discriminated differences in brightness as keenly as did the normals. It would have been expected that the same general factors which had been found to interfere with so many other variables would also have manifested themselves here. It is possible that the procedure used did not consider sufficiently the effect of the pre-adaptation level. Data which were obtained in another study (Clausen & Karrer, 1963) seemed to indicate this, but the consistency of the three retarded samples may suggest that this recording be repeated with a more rigorous procedure.

Both Muller-Lyer variables indicated that the retarded had the same amount of this illusion as the normals. Since the illusion is generally considered to develop with age, it is difficult to see why it should not have been impaired in the retardates. A highly speculative explanation would be that the result was caused by two factors: impaired development, which would have tended to give less illusion; this opposed by the factors of attention and motivation, which would have tended to increase the illusion score.

It is not easy to specify what the six variables have in common. One is considered a background variable; two—Two-Point Difference and Mirror Drawing Error Range—are derived scores which do not measure specific functions; while the last three belong to the perceptual domain. Since these six variables did not discriminate between the four samples, they are candidates for exclusion from the battery.

The remaining 44 variables did reach the F ratio at the 5% level or better. For these variables comparison of the sample means was made with the same statistical procedure as described for sex comparison. For each possible combination of samples the homogeneity of variance was determined. If variance ratio (F test) did not reach the 5% significance level, standard t test with pooled variances was used to determine differences between means. Where variance ratio exceeded the 5% level, variances were not pooled. Because of the multiple comparisons, the criterion for significance was set at the more stringent level of 1% rather than the 5% level used for analysis of variance. The results of these comparisons are included in Fig. 3.

Comparing Samples 1 and 4

A comparison of the youngest retarded sample with the control sample showed that in addition to the six nonsignificant variables mentioned above, there were five more variables which did not reach significance: Hand Dominance, Identification Threshold, Kinesthesis Left, Kinesthesis Right and Time Interval Estimation. The youngest retardates did not differ from their normal age group in the other expression of laterality; namely, Hand Dominance. Neither did they differ for one of the sensory variables; namely, Kinesthesis Right and Left. These two measures were among the few (a total of seven) where the youngest retardates performed better than the normals. Since the lack of difference from the normals occurred for independent measures on each side of the body, it did not seem to be a fortuitous finding. The two Kinesthesis measures were the only ones in the battery which showed significant differences between the normals and the two oldest retarded samples but not between the normals and the youngest retardates. Thus the finding did not seem to be related to attention or arousal factors. It seemed that performance level decreased with increasing age in retardates, but there are no data available to determine if the same trend occurs in normals.

Contrary to expectation, Identification Threshold and Time Interval Estimation were not significantly lower in the retardates. For the former measure the mean was lower but failed to reach significance because of the great variability among the retardates. Time Interval Estimation showed the retardates to reproduce the interval more accurately than the normals, who tended toward underestimation. In that the *SD* was greater in the retardates, variability of the ten reproductions by the subject may be a more appropriate measure for time estimation than is the mean. This problem will be further discussed in a separate article.

For the remaining 39 variables there were significant differences between the two samples. The 8-10 year old retardates differed decidedly from the age norm for motor and complex mental variables, for all but one sensory variable, and for most perceptual variables. They did not differ for laterality measures, for some derived variables (Two-Point Difference and Mirror Drawing Error Range), and for some perceptual variables which seemed to involve judgement of differences There were, however, many other variables which depended upon the same function but where significant differences did occur.

In recruiting subjects for the project, an attempt was made to include 8-10 year olds in both the youngest retarded and the normal samples. Since it proved impossible to find a sufficient number of the young retardates, the age restriction was not adhered to closely. The consequence was that the two samples which were supposed to be matched for chronological age turned out to be significantly different with respect to age. Since the retarded sample was somewhat older than the normal, the difference in performance level cannot be ascribed to difference in age.

Comparing Samples 2 and 4

The 12-15 year old retardates and normals were significantly different for PMA-MA, although they were intended to be matched. Two possible reasons for this discrepancy have been dealt with above: an unexpectedly low score for the retardates on PMA and a higher mean for MA than for CA in the normals. It is believed that the discrepancy between the MA of the two samples was artifically enhanced by the measure used, but the skewness of the normal sample is unequivocal.

Many significant differences in the 1-4 comparison had disappeared in the 2-4 comparison. Among the sensory variables, Color Vision, Speech Threshold, and Ataxiometry were no longer significantly different. It seems unlikely that the basic ability of color reception should be so delayed in retardates that it does not reach normal functioning level until after the age of 10. Since the testing of color vision in the Orthorater required the reading of numbers, it may be that difficulties with number reading were the actual reason for the impaired performance in the youngest retardates. That Threshold for Speech was no longer different from normals may be interpreted as improvement in listening technique (attention), rather than late development of the fundamental sensory mechanism.

Of the 18 motor variables, 13 were no longer significantly different, two became significantly higher than the normals' (Grip L and R), while only three remained significantly lower. This indicated development in motor variables which involved muscular strength and simple motor coordination (Ataxiometry and Grip), speech, and dexterity. As will be documented below, these motor variables continue to develop beyond the age of 10 in the normals also, and the fact that the 12-15 year old retardates functioned at the level of 8-10 year old normals did not mean that they had caught up with their own age norm. There were indications that they were as much behind a normal 12-15 sample as the 8-10 retardates were behind the 8-10 normals.

Two of the same perceptual measures in which the 8-10 retardates were not different from the normals—Identification Threshold and Time Interval—still failed to show significance for the 12-15 sample, and the previous comments apply to this situation as well. Stereognosis improved considerably. The rate of progress here was only parallelled in motor measures, and it is possible that this variable has enough of a motor component to have produced this result. In Weight Lifting the retardates were still strongly susceptible to the illusion, so that they severely underestimated the variable. They were a little less susceptible than were the 8-10 retardates, still more susceptible than were the normals, but not sufficiently more as to render the difference significant.

For 24 variables plus CA, the 12-15 retardates differed significantly from the normals. The significantly higher score for the two Grip measures reflected the late maturation of this function and showed the inadequacy of a younger normal sample as reference. Previous reports on Strength of Grip are reviewed below. Kinesthesis, which showed significant difference for this sample but not for Sample 1, has been discussed above. It seemed that this function matured early and started declining between the ages of 10 and 12.

For the remaining twenty variables Sample 2 as well as Sample 1 maintained poorer scores than did the normals. Among these variables were five sensory measures: Visual Acuity, Audiometry Left and Right, and Two-Point Left and Right; three motor measures: Lower Arm Movement, Hand Precision Hits, and Railwalking; seven perceptual measures: Word Association, Reaction Time to Pictures (Speed of Perception), Span of Apprehension, Recognition of Non-meaningful Material, Azimuth Arithmetic, Azimuth Reversals, and CFF; and all five measures of complex mental functions. While all categories of variables were represented, it is seen that there were relatively few motor variables whereas measures of sensory, perceptual, and complex mental functions were more strongly represented.

As mentioned previously, visual acuity was often difficult to determine because some of the retarded seemed to lack the concept of direction (up-down, right-left) which was required for correct identification of the critical areas. While this may have contributed somewhat to the low score in the youngest sample, it is doubtful that it accounted for the acuity score in the older samples, and it appears therefore that visual acuity is more often impaired among retardates than normals. A low pure tone threshold coexisting with a practically normal speech threshold has previously been interpreted to be a result of poor motivation or poor attention, rather than an actual sensory deficit. While the present survey of sensory functions was limited to a few modalities, there was clear evidence that some sensory functions in Sample 2 were impaired. It may be that the factors responsible for the lower scores on these measures were related to attention, motivation, self assertion, and the like. Lower scores in Sample 1 than in Sample 2 for Visual Acuity, Color Vision, Audiometry, and Speech Threshold, are consistent with this interpretation, as it does not seem likely that sensory functions should be affected by developmental factors between ages 8-10 and 12-15. It would be interesting to re-examine some of the younger subjects of the study four to five years after the original testing, under the assumption that there has been a development in attention or motivation but not any changes in the sensory mechanism per se.

While many of the motor skill tests which required hand-finger coordination differed significantly in Sample 1 but not in Sample 2, three motor variables maintained their significance. Lower Arm Movement seemed so difficult for the retardates to do that even though the 12-15 retardates had improved measurably over the 8-10 retardates, they did not reach the level of 8-10 normals. Because of the more proficient performance levels of some of the more complex motor tasks, Lower Arm Movement was regarded as reflecting effort or drive in addition to actual motor functioning.

Hand Precision Hits was a specific test of motor coordination which was not impaired in the sample, since the higher score in the normals was compensated for by more errors. Averaging Errors and Hits in Sample 2 gave a *T* score of 49. Thus it appears that a more cautious attitude rather than motor coordination was responsible for the lower score for Hand Precision Hits. The result of the Railwalking test indicated that the complex motor coordination and the necessary integration of visual cues were more profoundly disturbed in these retardates than was the fine coordination of hand and finger.

The majority of the perceptual tasks showed significant difference between Samples 2 and 4. The 12-15 retardates were slower than the normals in forming word association; they were slower to name an object; they had a narrower span of apprehension; they were not as proficient in recognizing nonmeaningful pictures or in reproducing the position of a slanting line; and their temporary resolution of light flashes as measured by CFF was not at the level of the 8-10 year old normals. It is by no means clear what differentiates between significant and nonsignificant perceptual tasks. It is suggested that in the latter category several tasks have an element of sensory discrimination and coordination while only CFF in the former category has this element. It may be that the nonsignificant measures represent a higher degree of task complexity, represented here by coordination of cues. This would tend to parallel the previous findings that retarded subjects do relatively better on complex motor tasks than they do for simple tasks. The relationship between Reaction Time to Pictures and Identification Threshold had some interesting points. Response initiation was crucial to the former but not to the latter, which required only passive attention. Since all three retarded samples performed significantly more poorly for Reaction Time to Pictures but not for Identification Threshold, there seemed to be a parallel to findings from motor functions, although it was not apparent from performance level means. This supports the notion that the retardates have particular difficulties with response initiation.

In the comparisons of these two samples, all the measures in the Complex Mental Function category were significantly different: Porteus MA, Porteus IQ, Raven, PMA-MA, and PMA-IQ.

In summary, it was found that the 12-15 year old retardates did not differ from the normals in laterality tasks. Several of the sensory variables were found to be inferior in the retardates but because of the constellation of the variables (poor Audiometer scores versus normal Speech score), and the improved performance as compared to Sample 1—this was interpreted to be due, at least in part, to general factors such as attention, motivation, self-assertion, etc. An exception to this may be Kinesthesis, which showed indications of being in a declining stage in retardates of this age. For those motor variables which depend upon muscular strength, simple coordination, speed, and dexterity, the sample had reached the performance level for the 8-10 year old normals, but probably not the level of normal 12-15 year olds. For variables which require complex motor coordination and integration of interoceptive and visual cues, and for tasks which rely heavily on self-assertion, they were still below the 8-10 normals. In some perceptual tasks the retardates did and in others they did not differ from normals. While it is difficult to see the distinction between the two groups of tasks, it is suggested that in tasks with an element of sensory discrimination and simple coordination they did not differ, while difference was seen in those tasks which required response initiation and a higher degree of coordination of cues.

For the complex mental tasks the 12-15 retardates were below the reference sample as indicated by MA and below their own age norm as indicated by IQ.

Comparing Samples 3 and 4

The oldest retarded sample had significantly poorer performance than the normals for the same 24 variables as did Sample 2 (see Fig. 3).

In addition there were seven significant differences, six of which were also significant in Sample 1. Ataxiometry M scores were significantly better than those of the normals. This was one of the few instances where the oldest retardates did better than the 12-15 sample. Ataxiometry L showed the same tendency, without reaching significance. Since Grip showed a similar pattern, it may be that improvement in Ataxiometry was related to development of muscular strength, which seemed to reach maturation later than any other function measured by the battery.

Three of the motor tasks regained significance, Visual RT, Auditory RT, and Scrambled RT; which simply means that the general lower performance level of the adult retardates, as compared with the 12-15 year old retardates, was sufficient to re-enter the realm of significance. The similar pattern of Stereognosis, the reverting to significance, may confirm the notion that this variable is strongly influenced by motor factors. Hand Precision Error was superior to the level of the normals, but Sample 3 made at the same time fewer attempts than did the normals. While fewer errors may have been a direct result of the few attempts, errors constituted 9% of the number of attempts in Sample 3, against 11% for the normal sample. This would indicate an overall higher precision in Sample 3, probably due to a more cautious attitude. Sample 2 performed very much like Sample 3 in this respect with an error percentage of 9.9. The youngest retardates scored lower than the normals both with regard to Hits and Errors, having an error percentage of 20.1 which was considerably poorer than any of the other samples, probably due to lack of motor development and less cautious attitude.

Sample 3 was the only one which differed from the normals in Time Interval Estimation. This difference resulted from their almost perfect mean reproduction (4.98 sec.) as contrasted to the underestimation of the normals (see Table 6). This may indicate an improvement with age of the ability to judge time among retarded subjects, but this finding should be confirmed before it is accepted.

For the remaining variables the discussion for Sample 2 applies to the adult retardates.

In summary, this sample was in most aspects like the 12-15 year olds, except that the general level was slightly lower, probably due to sampling factors. Ataxiometry, Grip, and Time Interval seemed to be more closely related to CA than MA. For some motor tasks "regression" was sufficient to produce significant differences from normals; task attitude, as indicated by the constellation of Hits and Errors for Hand Precision, appeared to be even more cautious.

Summary and Discussion

The comparison of three age groups of retardates with a group of 8-10 year old normals has shown seven variables in which the performance of the retardates did not differ from the normals. No difference was found between the proportion of left and right dominance, the difference between Two-Point Threshold on left and right sides, or reduction in number of errors over 10 trials of mirror drawing. For all three samples the mean for Identification was more than 1 *SD* below that of the normals, but the great variability in the retardates prevented this difference from being significant. Unexpectedly, the retardates were found to discriminate brightness differences better than did the normals. The three retarded samples were consistent in this trend, but it was not indicated in other discrimination tasks, such as Two-Point Threshold or Kinesthesis. While procedural factors, such as pre-adaptation, may have contributed to the results, it seems indicated that the Brightness Discrimination task should be administered to another group of retardates and compared with other tasks of simultaneous discrimination. The nonsignificant differences for the two Muller-Lyer variables showed that these retardates were no more susceptible to this type of visual illusion than were normals. If the Muller-Lyer illusion is related to experience in judging size-relations, it would appear that the retardates had acquired this experience.

Sensory variables in the retardates showed a tendency to improve with age but were generally below the normal level. Since it is unlikely that sensory functions should improve in the age groups in question, and since the constellation of impaired pure tone threshold and intact speech threshold posed particular problems, these findings may, in part at least, have resulted from difficulties in sustained attention to the task at hand. The lack of concept of directions has already been discussed with regard to the Visual Acuity task. The most rational approach to the problem would be to develop procedures for the measurement of sensory functions with a minimum demand on attention.

Muscular strength appeared to be characterized by a particularly late maturation point. It has been indicated that this function determines the functional level of Grip, Ataxiometry, and possibly also Stereognosis. While the older retardates may have surpassed the 8-10 year old normals for these variables, the available literature suggests that they were as much behind their own age norm as were the youngest retardates.

The motor functions which reflect dexterity, fine motor coordination, speed of movement, alertness, and response initiation were severely impaired but improved with age, as they do in normals. The variables which depend heavily on response initiation and alertness seemed particularly impaired. All three retarded samples showed a trend toward better performance with increased complexity of motor tasks;

the two factors of response initiation and the greater attentional demands (or arousal value) of the more complex tasks may have been involved in this. Performance level for tasks which involved gross motor coordination or coordination and integration of proprioceptive and visual cues (railwalking), was below the normals for all three retarded samples. The improvement of motor abilities with age resulted in fewer significant differences in the older samples. Related to sampling factors, the oldest retardates showed a tendency to "regression" which increased the number of significant differences.

It may be interesting to contrast Ataxiometry (static steadiness) where the retardates functioned close to normals, with Railwalking (dynamic steadiness) where they did poorly. Further experimentation is necessary to determine whether this difference was due to essential characteristics of the tasks: muscular strength or coordination in balancing on the floor; visual components of Railwalking which are not present in Ataxiometry; or the dynamic aspects of kinesthetic feedback involved in Railwalking.

The perceptual measures showed less consistency of patterns than did the motor variables, and there was less increase in level across the three age groups. As documented in a subsequent section, there is evidence from the literature that normal subjects also have less protracted development for perceptual than for motor functions. Several perceptual variables in the present study were significantly below the normals in all retarded samples, while for others there was no difference among the samples. Time Interval and Weight Lifting showed difference for one, but not for the other two retarded samples. It is difficult to identify the characteristics of the variables which do and do not differ. It may be indicated that variables which depend upon sensory discrimination, quantitative judgement, and motor coordination differ, while the variables which require higher degree of coordination of clues and integration do not differ. Hence a parallel to the relationship between performance level and complexity of motor variables is suggested.

To some extent the motor and perceptual tasks which did and did not differ between retardates and normals followed the distinction which has been made between passive reception of sensory stimuli, facilitating environmental intake, and active attention, which rejects external stimuli (Lacey, 1959; Obrist, 1963). It seems that the latter function was more impaired in the retardates than was the former.

As would be expected, the complex mental measures were all below the normal level, and the pattern was generally the same in the three retarded samples. The MAs were higher than the IQs, especially for the two older samples, and for the PMA variables. The difference between Porteus and Raven was slight, indicating that the measures which involve form perception and relationship in space were less impaired than the multifactor PMA. This problem is further discussed in a separate article (Clausen, 1965).

Several tests have been found which do not seem to discriminate between normals and retardates, and others which do not seem to measure the functions they were intended to measure. This would suggest that the following tests may be dropped from the battery:

Hand Dominance
Eye Dominance
Identification Threshold
Brightness Discrimination
Time Interval Estimation
Muller-Lyer
Perimetry

It should be noted that these conclusions are tentative in that they have reference only to the general discrimination between normal and retarded samples. It is definitely possible that some of the variables in this list may have significance in defining subgroups of the mentally retarded or be of importance in evaluating an individual.

A survey of the profiles of individual subjects indicated that the most prevalent characteristics of the group patterns are found in the majority of retardates. It is therefore difficult to see that the existing constellations of impaired and intact functions in general indicate localized cortical dysfunction. It seems more reasonable that some general factor, or factors, are operating which, to a greater or lesser extent, are involved in all variables. The fact that some—but not other—sensory variables are involved makes us hesitate to assume that a number of independent factors, such as an auditory factor, a motor factor, etc., may be impaired. It is difficult to find a common denominator for the variables we have described as impaired, but two suggestions may be offered. The first is the readiness of the organism to respond to outside stimuli and the ability to focus the attention on a task for a sustained period of time. The other is the limitation of the retardates to integrate cues when they exceed a certain degree of complexity; i.e., the harmonious synthesis of differentiated functions. The above data are therefore being interpreted to indicate impairment of the arousal mechanism as a central characteristic of the type of retarded subjects included in this study. It is furthermore assumed that various tasks differ in their demand on self-initiated arousal.

Simple and monotonous tasks require a high degree of arousal for adequate performance. If the ambition of the subject cannot supply this arousal level, the performance level will be low. More challenging, and perhaps more complex, tasks will more easily evoke arousal in the individual and are not as much dependent on the ability of the subject to control his arousal level. Thus pure tone audiometry fails, where speech threshold approaches normal level, and complex motor tasks are relatively better performed than simple tasks. If, however, the complexity of the tasks makes too great a demand on the ability to integrate separate functions, then the handicap of the retardates is readily manifested. This has already been indicated—for instance, for Railwalking and the complex mental functions. Thus there seems to be an intermediate level of complexity where the retardates function optimally.

COMPARISON OF RETARDATES TO NORMALS

Several indications have been noted that the retarded samples differed among themselves, partly, at least, as a result of growth. It would therefore be pertinent to consider a comparison of the three retarded samples. It may be legitimate, however, to question whether these samples differed only with respect to chronological age or whether they differed along other dimensions. As can be seen from Fig. 3, Sample 1 differed significantly from both Samples 2 and 3 with regard to IQ. We know from Table 2 that the male-female ratio varied in the three retarded samples, and it is possible that the etiological composition was not equivalent. Because of this, 40 retarded subjects from each age group, D1, D2, and D3, were drawn in such a fashion that they were matched for IQ, male-female ratio, and etiological composition in order to constitute developmental samples.

In the selection procedure, subjects with missing scores were first eliminated. As a result of the selection, mean CA changed from 115 to 117, from 168 to 166, from 260 to 256 in Samples 1, 2, and 3 respectively. Similar changes for IQ were from 57.3 to 58.6, from 51.9 to 56.7, and from 48.6 to 54.1; and for MA from 65 to 68, from 85 to 92, and from 88 to 97. While CA remained rather constant, there was an increase in MA, nonsignificant for D1 but significant at the 1% level for D2 and D3. As a result of the increased MA there was also an increase in IQ. Again, this increase was nonsignificant for D1, but reached the 5% level for D2, and the 1% level for D3.

T scores for all 50 variables in the developmental samples are presented in Fig. 4. In order to ascertain how well the developmental samples represented the total sample, the differences in *T* scores have

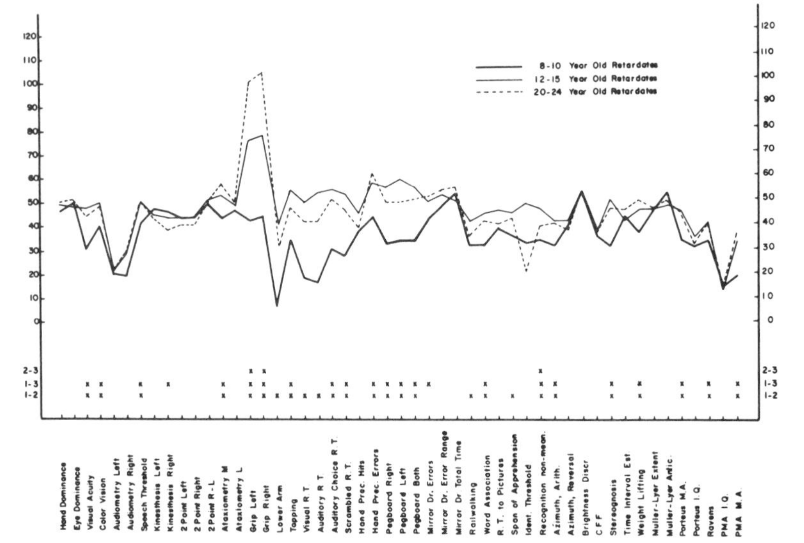

Figure 4. Group means for the three developmental samples (N=40) plotted in terms of mean and standard deviation of the total normal sample. The x marks indicate where differences between the developmental samples reach the 1% level of significance.

been computed and entered in Table 8. The table shows a general tendency toward increase in scores in the developmental samples, apparently related to increases in MA and IQ. This increase, for the most part rather modest, is reasonably equally distributed throughout the three samples and over all types of measurement. The mean increase in *T* scores is 2.7, 3.8, and 3.6 for the three samples respectively. The motor tasks contributed more to this increase than did any of the other domains. Correlation coefficients (Pearson) between the developmental and total samples were found to be .98, .95, and .96 respectively. As was found for the total samples, Kendall's coefficient of concordance for the three developmental samples was significant beyond the .001 level of confidence (Chi Square equals 107.5 for 50 *df*). This indicates that the pattern of scores between the two sets of samples was similar. The developmental samples, as representative of the total samples, may be summarized as follows: they had a tendency to higher scores, significant for some motor measures in D2 and D3. This upward shift made D2 exceed the normals for several motor variables and brought D3 in closer approximation with the normals. Where changes occurred they had more often a tendency to augment developmental trend. The original patterns of scores were well maintained in the developmental sample.

The developmental samples were analyzed in exactly the same way

TABLE 8

Difference in *T* Score Between Developmental Samples and Total Samples for the Retardates

Test	*8–10*	*12–15*	*20–24*
Hand Dom.	1.1	.1	1.3
Eye Dom.	−.2	−.7	1.6
Visual Acuity	2.6	5.9	4.5
Color Vision	.3	4.2	3.0
Audio. L	5.4	2.2	6.2
Audio. R	4.1	6.1	8.7
Speech Thres.	.6	2.4	3.1
Kinesth. L	1.0	0.0	1.0
Kinesth. R	1.2	1.2	−3.0
2-Point L	1.3	.4	0.0
2-Point R	.9	1.3	.2
2-Point R-L	−.6	.9	−.7
Atax. M	1.9	.6	1.3
Atax. L	1.6	.3	.9
Grip L	2.2	4.0	10.7
Grip R	2.8	5.4	12.5
Lower Arm	11.6	12.4	13.6
Tapping	3.9	10.5	5.5
Vis. RT	12.4	8.1	8.8
Audio. RT	12.6	11.0	9.2
Aud. Choice RT	6.4	7.3	12.6
Scrambled RT	5.4	7.5	6.3
Hand Prec. Hits	5.0	−.2	1.4
Hand Prec. Err.	2.2	4.4	2.6
Pegboard R	4.7	7.7	3.3
Pegboard L	4.4	8.7	1.6
Pegboard B	6.0	7.1	5.3
Mirr. Dr. Err.	−.5	3.5	6.1
Mirr. Dr. Err. Ra.	−1.7	.7	4.5
Mirr. Dr. T.T.	−2.4	−1.4	3.4
Railwalking	3.2	4.8	1.6
Word Assoc.	.6	1.9	1.4
Percep. Speed	3.6	4.1	3.8
Span of Appreh.	4.9	3.1	3.0
Ident. Thresh.	−2.5	10.6	−8.1
Recogn.	.6	4.4	2.2
Azimuth Arith.	2.4	3.0	3.0
Azimuth Rev.	6.0	3.6	5.9
Brightn. Discr.	−.4	12.4	.2
CFF	−.3	1.4	2.3
Stereogn.	6.4	4.9	7.8
Time Int. Est.	1.4	−2.0	5.4
Weight Lift.	2.2	.5	−4.3
Muller-L. Ext.	2.6	.7	2.0
Muller-L. Antic.	1.3	.6	−.7
Porteus M.A.	2.2	4.2	4.8
Porteus I.Q.	1.7	3.2	3.1
Raven	.9	1.1	3.1
PMA I.Q.	.9	3.3	3.8
PMA M.A.	1.7	4.4	6.1
CA	2.8	−2.6	−4.9

as were the total samples, with an analysis of variance for each variable. The *F*s from these analyses are listed in Table 7, and the occurrence of significant differences between means, using 1% level as confidence criterion, is included in Fig. 4.

From Table 7 it may be seen that there are fewer significant *F*s for the developmental than for the total sample, mainly because the normal sample was not involved in this analysis. A comparison of the indications of significance in Fig. 4 with the corresponding data in Fig. 3 will show that there is essential agreement between the two Figures. But few significant differences have been lost and even fewer gained. The changes tend to make D2 and D3 more equal in the comparison with D1.

In conclusion, the dominant characterics of the comparisons in the total sample were carried over to the developmental sample. The general trends were more consistent in the developmental sample than they were in the total sample; less exceptions occurred. For this reason further discussion of developmental trends will be limited to the developmental sample.

The variables in which D1 differed significantly from D2 and D3 can be seen in Fig. 4. They constitute the variables which had maximum discrimination power between the retarded subjects. Neither Hand nor Eye Dominance discriminated between developmental samples. A few of the sensory measures showed significant difference, Visual Acuity, Color Vision, and Speech Threshold. These variables were among the purest sensory measures but did not seem to be uniform in their demand on alertness. Most of the significant differences were for motor variables, particularly those which were related to muscular strength, coordination of small muscle groups, and dexterity. The muscular strength of the oldest sample was still above that of the 12-15 sample—reflected in Grip and Ataxiometry M—but the relative position for these two samples, with regard to the relationship between Stereognosis and muscular strength, was not confirmed. This variable, however, still had a pattern which resembled the motor more than the perceptual variables. About one-third of the perceptual variables showed significant difference in this comparison: Word Association, Recognition of Non-meaningful Material, Azimuth Arithmetic, Stereognosis, and Weight Lifting. While not consistently so, there was a tendency for the perceptual measures which differentiated to be more complex than those which did not differentiate. The latter seemed more to reflect simple judgement of qualitative relations. As would be expected, complex mental functions, except when related to chronological age, tended to develop with age in the present population. For all of these comparisons D1 had poorer scores than the other two samples.

In addition there were some variables where D2 but not D3 differed significantly from D1. These variables were: Span of Apprehension, Railwalking, Lower Arm Movement, Visual RT, and Auditory RT. Characteristic for all but one of these measures in which D3 seemed to deteriorate was that they were motor measures. The measures ranged from task-simplicity to the more complex Railwalking. Thus it seemed that motor measures were less stable than were the other measures; showing the most impressive development gains but also most deterioration beyond a critical age.

For two measures D3—but not D2—differed from D1, namely Mirror Drawing Errors and Kinesthesis R. For Mirror Drawing Errors D3 had the best scores among the retardates. Apparently this characteristic continued to develop to adult age. Since Mirror Drawing Errors was significantly different but not Mirror Drawing Time, this would indicate that the role of task attitude was minimized, and that the relationship between motor coordination and interference effect of previously established eye-hand coordination was modified. From the present data it is not possible to say which of the two factors is primarily responsible.

Hand Precision Errors showed the same trend of performance. Kinesthesis R was particularly interesting in that it showed a reversed developmental trend, with D3 having inferior performance as compared to D1, and D2 occupying the intermediate position. Thus the findings showed that this skill deteriorated with age. By examining Fig. 4 it may be seen that the same trend was present for Kinesthesis L, Two-Point R, and Two-Point L—all of which belong to the proprioceptive modalities. Parietal lobe impairment could thus be indicated but other variables which presumably involve the same cortical area (e.g., Stereognosis) made it difficult to reach a firm conclusion.

Fig. 4 shows that there were many variables which revealed no significant differences between the three retarded samples. These measures represented functions which showed no significant development with age in the mentally retarded. Such measures may be grouped in two different categories: those with no difference from normals and those where the retardates of all three age samples remain below the performance level of the normal 8-10 year olds. Marked differences in developmental patterns for motor, perceptual, and sensory tasks emerged; the main difference being that the developmental trends leveled off much earlier for sensory and perceptual tasks than they did for motor tasks. This is believed to be the case also for normals, but the point is difficult to document, since textbook authors in developmental psychology have not seemed concerned with the difference in maturation time for different types of functions. As will be seen below, there is a considerable amount of evidence for development of motor functions up to adolescence. Information about maturation for sensory and perceptual measures is not easy to find, but indication of earlier maturation of these functions has been found for Span of Apprehension (Woodworth, 1938), CFF (e.g., Meili & Tobler, 1931; Miller, 1942; Csank & Lehman, 1958), Weight Lifting (Gilbert, 1894) and Muller-Lyer Illusion (Walters, 1942; Wapner & Werner, 1957).

Ataxiometry in the median and lateral planes had different developmental trends; the former improved with age, whereas the latter hardly differed from the normal sample. It would seem that lateral sway would be an essential component in Railwalking, but the two measures, as previously discussed, were in contrast in differentiating normals from retardates.

Turning now to a comparison of D2 and D3 one may see from Fig. 4 that for most measures D2 had a higher score than D3. This trend was reversed with continued development up to adult level, for Laterality, Audiometry, Body Sway, Grip, Hand Precision Errors, Mirror Drawing, Time Interval, and Weight Lifting. Only Grip L and R reached significant proportions, with Ataxiometry M approaching significance. The three measures with substantial difference between D2 and D3 involved muscular strength, since it has been pointed out that motor variables which measure manipulative and locomotive tasks very consistently declined in the oldest sample. Apparently muscular strength and the type of coordination which is required to maintain balance are only remotely related to manipulation and locomotion in the retardates.

Recognition of Non-meaningful material showed significant decline between D2 and D3. While lower performance level in D3 was found for the majority of the measures, especially for motor tasks, the decline reached significance only for Recognition of Non-meaningful Material. From the comparisons of the three developmental samples of retarded subjects it may be concluded that different developmental trends were present:

1. Continued development up to adult age, characteristic for muscular strength, static equilibrium, and weight-size illusion; or up to age 12-15, characteristic for Color Vision, Speech Threshold, Hand Precision, and intellectual functions.

2. Development to age 12-15 followed by a decline—although generally not significant—found for speed, manipulation, and dynamic equilibrium of the motor measures, and for some perceptual measures of a complex nature. [It should be recalled that, as indicated in Fig. 2, the males may have been primarily responsible for this decline. It is still an open question as to whether this pattern represented a genuine developmental decline or was a result of selection factors, in the sense that the retardates above 20 who remain in an institution are those with generally impaired level of functioning, regardless of IQ.]

3. Gradual decline with age suggested for Kinesthesis and cutaneous space discrimination.

4. No developmental trends but departure from normals, characteristic for pure tone threshold and some perceptual variables which seemed to require simple judgement of qualitative relations.

5. No developmental trends but similarity to normals, including laterality and some perceptual measures which seemed to require judgement of quantitative relations.

Thus it appears that development differs considerably for the various functions, and that it is an oversimplification to call the mental retardates slow developers. In the first place, rate of development varies, as has just been demonstrated, and secondly, the retardates seldom reach the functioning level of their normal peers.

Confirmation and further study of these trends in relation to normals seem to be of some importance.

TOTAL ABILITY SCORES AND ACROSS-TRAIT VARIABILITY

As mentioned under Sex Comparison, each subject's mean of the 48 variables and the *SD*s of these scores around their own Mean (across-trait variability) have been considered. The sample means of these Mean *T* score and *T* score *SD* are entered in Table 9 for the developmental and total samples.

The distribution of these *T* score means and *SDs* for the total samples are plotted in Fig. 5. The normals showed fairly normal dis-

TABLE 9

GROUP MEANS OF MEAN *T* SCORE AND *SD* OF *T* SCORE FOR TOTAL AND DEVELOPMENTAL SAMPLES

	Sample 1	*Sample 2*	*Sample 3*	*Sample 4*
Mean T Score				
Boys	34.9	43.4	39.8	50.2
Girls	33.0	41.9	42.6	49.8
Total	34.4	42.9	40.7	50.0
Developmental	37.2	46.4	44.1	—
SD of T Scores				
Boys	22.4	18.1	20.4	9.4
Girls	21.9	16.6	20.5	9.3
Total	22.3	17.6	20.4	9.4
Developmental	19.8	15.2	18.9	—

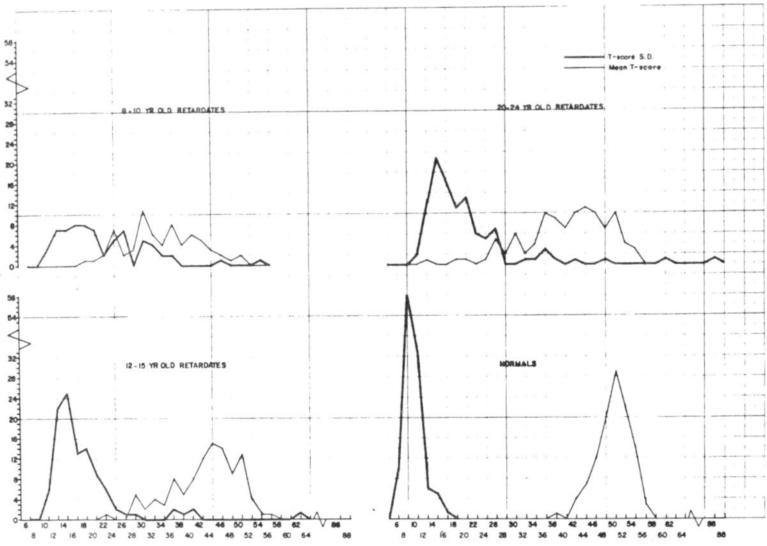

Figure 5. Distribution of Mean *T* score and *T* score *SD* for the four samples.

tribution of both of these measures with relatively limited range. In contrast to this, the retardates had considerably lower values for the *T* score means, and higher Standard Deviations, as may be seen from Table 9 and Fig. 5. While the distribution of their means was fairly normal, and the distribution of their *SD*s was skewed upwards, both measures had substantially greater ranges than had measures of the normals. There appeared to be some developmental improvement up to 12-15, but not beyond.

Thus the retardates were less homogeneous than the normals in two aspects: In the first place, the overall ability, as measured by the test battery, varied considerably more in the retardates. *SD* of the group means was 7.4 in the youngest retardates, 6.7 in the 12-15, 8.3 in the 20-24, and 3.4 in the normals. Secondly, the retardates showed a much higher across-trait variability than did the normals. It seems more difficult to predict general ability level from a few indices in retardates than in normals. The *SD* for IQ was greater in the normals than in the retardates; so the greater variability in Mean and *SD* for *T* score was not caused by greater variability in intelligence.

While the higher across-trait variability in the retardates carries the promise of differential profiles for subgroups of retardates, the possibility of a fairly standard retardate profile exists, with differences primarily in levels.

When the results of individual subjects were perused, indication was found of an inverse relation between Mean and *SD* of *T*. The correlation between these two measures was therefore ascertained for the four samples—with males and females separated, as well as combined. The correlation between each of these measures and IQ was also determined. These data are presented in Table 10.

TABLE 10

CORRELATIONS BETWEEN MEAN *T* SCORES, *SD* OF *T* SCORES, AND PMA-IQ

	Boys			*Girls*			*Boys & Girls*		
	Mean vs SD	*Mean vs IQ*	*IQ vs SD*	*Mean vs SD*	*Mean vs IQ*	*IQ vs SD*	*Mean vs SD*	*Mean vs IQ*	*IQ vs SD*
8-10 Retarded	−.80**	.63**	−.58**	−.85**	.46*	−.32	−.79**	.57**	−.52**
12-15 Retarded	−.57**	.81**	−.52**	−.48*	.58**	−.19	−.53**	.70**	−.30*
20-24 Retarded	−.76**	.72**	−.57**	−.74**	.65**	−.29	−.70**	.65**	−.33**
Normals	−.23	.51**	−.04	−.42**	.62**	−.39*	−.37**	.55**	−.18

* significant at 1%
** significant at .1%

An inverse relationship existed between Mean and *SD* of *T* for both boys and girls. It is obvious that this relationship was closer for the retardates than for the normals. There was in fact a relationship between these correlation coefficients and the magnitude of the Mean and *SD* in the four samples, so that Sample 1 had the highest coefficient and the lowest general level. The negative correlation indicated that there was no regular occurrence of low scores for all measures. An overall low *T* score was contributed to heavily by relatively few marked deviant scores, which at the same time increased the *SD*. It was this irregular deviation from the normals which seemed to characterize many retardates, particularly at a young age. It should be noted, as is evident from Fig. 5, that the variability itself varied among the retardates. One is thus concerned with intra- as well as inter-variability of test scores. Whether these features are sufficiently regular to serve as a basis for sub-grouping is a question which will be discussed in a later section.

All correlation coefficients between IQ and mean *T* scores were positive and significant. The correlation coefficient for normal boys was slightly lower than for normal girls, while all three retarded samples had higher correlation coefficients for the boys. This sex difference was not easy to explain. Combining boys and girls resulted in rather similar correlation coefficients for the normal and the youngest retarded samples, while its effects in the two older retarded samples produced somewhat higher correlations. Thus level of IQ seemed to be related to overall performance level on the test battery. It may be that the tasks of the battery are basic to intelligent behavior, and that the more intact the sensory, motor, and perceptual functions are, the better equipped the subject is to cope with abstract tasks which are included in the intelligence scale.

Since the correlation coefficients were higher for the older retardates than for the younger, it may be argued that the relationship lags with decrease in the ability of understanding the instructions. This interpretation was not supported by the normals, who had a higher mean MA than any of the retarded samples. Neither was the overall lower correlation in the normals to be explained by a lower standard deviation of IQ in this group, since Table 6 shows the *SD* of IQ to have been slightly higher in the normals than in the retardates. The low variability among the normals for Mean *T* score, as is evident from Fig. 5, did contribute to their lower correlation.

The corresponding correlation between IQ and *SD* of *T* showed consistent negative relationship. An inverse relationship between IQ and *SD* of *T* was indicated, stronger in retarded boys than in retarded girls, and missing in normal boys. Previous comments to relationships between Mean *T* and *SD* of *T* apply also to this finding.

In summary, the retardates varied more in overall ability level and across-trait variability than the normals. Both variables were correlated to IQ, the former directly and the latter inversely in the retardates, with a stronger relationship among the boys than among the girls. In the normals the relationships were in the same direction, were less strong than in the retardates, and, in contrast to the retardates, stronger for the girls than for the boys.

REVIEW OF THE RESPECTIVE VARIABLES IN RELATION TO PREVIOUSLY REPORTED FINDINGS

With a battery of tests as extensive as that of the ASP, the task of relating the present findings to those reported in the literature becomes quite a problem. So many studies are relevant that a literature review could easily be overly extensive. The general necessity for a literature review is lessened by the fact that several recent reviews have been compiled; e.g., Gallagher (1957), Clarke and Clarke (1958), and Jordan (1961). Also extensive reviews have recently been published by Ellis (1963), and Stevens and Heber (1964). The primary concern with the present survey has therefore been to provide a comparison between test results of the present study and results obtained by other investigators for similar tasks with retarded populations. Another major concern has been with the correspondence of the present results of the normals to those previously obtained, and with evidence in the literature concerning developmental trends. The latter is of particular significance for the comparison of the 8-10 year old normals to the older retarded samples.

The sequence of the variables which are covered is the same as that in the description of the battery and in the tables and figures.

Laterality. According to criterion for Hand Dominance given in the Testing section of Chapter II, the data of the present study shown in Table 11 indicate that the 12-15 retarded sample had a smaller percentage of left dominance than had any of the other samples. It also appears that the retardates were more often ambidextrous than were the normals, particularly the youngest retardates. This may indicate that retardates are not as successful as normals in establishing hand dominance; as more of them remain ambidextrous. With respect to Eye Dominance, there was little difference between normals and retardates. For combined hand and eye laterality, there were fewer 8-10 year old retardates who showed dominance for both right eye and hand, which was counterbalanced by heavier representation in the miscellaneous category; again indicating less success in establishment of dominance. According to Tredgold (1947, p. 131), Ireland observed in 1898 that considerably more retardates than normals are ambidex-

TABLE 11

DISTRIBUTION (IN PER CENT) FOR THE FOUR SAMPLES OVER CATEGORIES OF HANDEDNESS, EYE DOMINANCE, AND THE TWO LATERALITY MEASURES COMBINED

	Handedness			*Eye Dominance*		
	Left	*Mixed*	*Right*	*Left*	*Mixed*	*Right*
8–10 Ret.	21	28	51	38	10	51
12–15 Ret.	12	10	77	42	6	52
20–24 Ret.	18	10	72	40	13	48
Normal	21	3	76	43	8	49

COMBINED

	R Hand—R Eye	*L Hand—L Eye*	*Cross Lat.*	*Miscel.*
8–10 Ret.	28	10	27	35
12–15 Ret.	45	8	32	15
20–24 Ret.	36	10	35	19
Normal	43	12	34	11

trous. Of 39 retarded cases with birth lesion, Doll (1933) found 41% to be left handed, 50% right handed and the remainder ambidextrous. With a median CA of 16 years and median IQ of 55, the higher percent of left handedness is probably explained by the more severe neurological involvement in Doll's subjects. Thus there is agreement between the present and previous studies that right hand dominance is less common in retardates than in normals.

Vision. Visual Acuity, in terms of group average, has been found to be lower in retardates than in normals. As has been discussed elsewhere, the Orthorater may not be the preferred technique for recording visual performance in retardates. In particular, the low score for the youngest retardates may be attributed to problems in understanding the instructions and properly indicating the location of the checkerboard. It appears, however, that occurrence of insufficient visual acuity is more frequent among the retardates. The data has also been distributed over categories of visual acuity as provided by Bausch and Lomb's standard for elementary schools; desirable visual performance, substandard performance, and seriously lowered visual performance. The percentage distribution is seen in Table 12. It is seen that the retardates, and particularly the youngest retardates, more frequently had substandard visual acuity than did the normals.

With respect to color vision Kratter (1957) has reported that color vision among high grade retardates equals approximately that of the normal population. The incidence rate among 63 male imbeciles was found to be 7.9% or about twice that of high grades. O'Connor (1957) reported very similar results: Incidence among eighty feebleminded did not exceed the 8% he found for normals while 13% of 144 imbeciles were color blind. If color blindness is defined as two or less figures correctly read, the percentages in the present study are 31, 19, 18, and 6% for the four samples respectively. Thus the ASP data

TABLE 12

DISTRIBUTION IN PER CENT OVER CATEGORIES OF VISUAL ACUITY AND COLOR VISION

	VISION			*COLOR VISION*		
	Good	*Marginal*	*Poor*	*Good*	*Marginal*	*Poor*
8–10 Ret.	32	40	28	35	34	31
12–15 Ret.	67	26	7	58	22	19
20–24 Ret.	63	20	17	63	19	18
Normal	92	8	—	73	21	6

showed more difference between normals and retardates than did the data of Kratter and O'Connor. While some of this discrepancy may be accounted for by the fact that our youngest subjects were younger than either Kratter's or O'Connor's, it does not account for the discrepancies at the older age levels.

Hearing. In the auditory tests a pattern of discrepancy between threshold for pure tone and speech was found in all retarded samples.

The score for hearing loss was computed by means of the Maico Slide-rule and included the value of the loss pad which was used to allow increasing as well as decreasing intensity variation. Since this prevented a direct comparison of data with those of other authors, hearing loss has been determined for the data when corrected for the value of the loss pad. The criterion for pure tone hearing loss was 20 db or greater for any two frequencies in the 500-800 cps range in one ear; for speech hearing loss it was 20 db below mean threshold of the normal sample. The results are seen in Table 13. The difference in hearing loss as defined by pure tone and speech threshold was again clear. The occurrence of pure tone loss among the retardates was not as great as has been reported by some other investigators. Birch and Matthews (1951) found that 54% of retarded subjects in the 10-19 age range and median IQ of 49 had moderate, while 32.7% had severe hearing loss. Foale and Paterson (1954) reported that, of 100 boys in the 10-19 age range with mean IQ of 66, 33% had some degree of hearing loss. Their lower incident rate was explained by the higher IQ of their subjects. Johnston and Farrell's (1954) study indicated that, in a group of 270 children with a mean CA of 13.2 and mean IQ of 61, 24% had hearing loss. This is approximately five times the incidence of hearing loss among public school children of comparable age. Schlanger (1953) reported hearing loss among 30% of 74 children in the 8-10 year range with IQs above 40. In a later study Schlanger and Gottsleben (1956) found, among 498 subjects with mean CA of 28.9 years and MA of 7.8, that 16.5% were non-testable, 14%

TABLE 13

OCCURRENCE (IN PER CENT) OF HEARING LOSS IN THE FOUR SAMPLES

	8–10 Retarded	*12–15 Retarded*	*20–24 Retarded*	*Normal*
Audiometry	23.5	16.2	20.4	.9
Speech Threshold	16.2	7.6	8.7	1.8
Both	7.3	4.8	5.8	0

had slight losses at the extreme frequencies, and 35% had hearing losses varying from moderate to deaf. Recently Rigrodsky, Prunty, & Glovsky (1961) found hearing loss in 25% of 325 retarded subjects ranging in age from 5 to 71 and with a wide range of IQ. The present author had an occasion to administer audiometer and speech threshold tests to a psychotic population as part of an evaluation procedure of psychosurgery (King & Clausen, 1956). At that time we were much impressed by the consistency of the speech thresholds in rather deteriorated schizophrenics, while pure tone audiograms seemed to be more easily influenced by internal and external events. These experiences were the reason for including the speech threshold test in the Ability Structure Project battery, and it has indeed paid off.

Davis and Silverman (1960) stated that children who were uncertain and erratic in their responses to variation in pure tone testing were also erratic in objective test response (GSR and EEG techniques). This might indicate that attention is a factor also in the objective test, or that the erratic performance may have a more profound physiological reason.

A more extensive review of the literature on the problem of incidence rate of hearing loss in the mentally retarded was given in a recently published monograph by Schlanger (1961). He listed 14 studies on the problem, and all showed considerably higher incidence of hearing loss among the retardates than among normals of comparable age. As pointed out by Schlanger, the difference found among these studies may readily be explained by difference in technique, criteria for hearing loss, and age, intellectual level, and organicity of the subjects studied. It is important to note that, with one exception, all the studies surveyed by Schlanger utilized pure tone rather than speech as stimulus. The ASP data would strongly suggest that high incidence of hearing loss was to some extent a result of the pure tone technique, and that the result would have been different if speech threshold had been used. Schlanger's (1961) data support the ASP's in this respect. He administered a battery of six hearing tests (standard audiometry air conduction, ear choice audiometry, play audiometry, standard bone conduction audiometry, GSR audiometry, and a speech reception test) to 65 subjects who failed to respond, or responded erroneously, in a screening audiometry test. Mean CA was 15.6 and mean IQ was 36.3. The tests were administered on three occasions: prior to, at the midpoint of, and following a seven-month listening training program. He found that the speech reception test initially gave the best threshold (14.7 db as against 25.9 db for standard audiometry), and was largely unchanged in the course of the program, while standard audiometry dropped slightly (22.6 db). Also, some individuals who were not testable with standard audiometric technique did respond on the speech reception test. Schlanger concluded: "On the basis of reliability of threshold results, overall period of testing, validity of responses and number of subjects able to be tested, the Speech Reception Threshold Test was suggested as the best choice for evaluating the hearing of retarded children," and "It can be suggested that speech audiometry may approach more closely to these subjects' auditory thresholds than the pure tone test mentioned above." Thus there is considerable agreement between Schlanger's study and the present one.

Further support comes from the review article by Reichstein and Rosenstein (1964) where reference is made to Hardy, who observed that a warbled tone has been found to be more effective than a steady tone because it is an attention-getting device. These reviewers also quoted several other authors to the effect that better response was obtained to speech sounds than to pure tones, in young children, in retarded children, and in brain-injured children.

The problem then is to account for the discrepancy between results in pure tone and in speech threshold. Relevant to high threshold for pure tone, Myklebust (1954) has observed that listening ability matures long after the hearing mechanism is developed. Schlanger (1961) thinks it is related to the learning and mental maturational deficit of the retardates, more specifically to the factors of attention and understanding by the subject of what is required of him. He believes that non-auditory variables to a large extent are responsible for the high pure tone threshold. Schlanger suggested that the discrepancy is a result of the unfamiliarity of the pure tone, whereas speech reception testing is concerned with understanding rather than detectability. He arrived at these conclusions by employing techniques which are part of retardates' communication system (pointing to a familiar picture when the name of the subject is presented). The slight reduction in pure tone threshold after training partially supported Schlanger in this supposition, but the fact that the pure tone threshold was still substantially higher than the speech threshold seems to indicate that additional explanation is required.

Reed (1961), surveying a child guidance population, also found a group of individuals (IQ below 75) with discrepancies between pure tone and speech threshold. In about half the cases he found speech threshold higher than pure tone threshold. Reed discussed these data in terms of perceptual defense and observed that the pure tone testing situation demands "vigilance."

With regard to difference between pure tone and speech threshold, there are other factors than lack of familiarity with the pure tone stimulus that might be considered. It is possible that the relative unresponsiveness to pure tones is not limited to this stimulus alone. We believe we have evidence that there are parallel situations in motor responses, which may indicate that we are dealing with a more general characteristic of the mentally retarded, or of certain groups of mental retardates. This will be further discussed subsequently.

Kinesthesis. For both Kinesthesis scores (R and L) the two older—but not the younger—retarded samples had significantly poorer performance than the normals. Since the recording technique used was designed for the present study, comparable data cannot be found in the literature. While etiological groups failed to show significant differences, Satter and Cassel (1955) found differences between organics and familials in ability to make tactual-kinesthetic localization on skin areas. The discrepancies with the present findings will be discussed below under the heading "Comparison between etiological groups."

Two-Point Threshold. All three retarded samples had performance level below the normals for right and left arm separately, but not for the difference between them. If the higher threshold had been due to focal cortical impairment it would not be expected that such impairment were regularly bilateral and the retardates therefore would have had a significantly higher difference score. That this was not the case makes it reasonable to seek another explanation than focal cortical damage. With respect to the normals, Semmes, Wienstein, Ghent, and Teuber (1960) reported on 33 normal adult males. Two-Point threshold measured along the longitudinal axis of the palm gave means of 14.6 and 13.9 mm and *SD*s of 4.7 and 2.5 for right and left hand respectively. The means corresponded rather closely to those found for the ASP normal sample, but the variability was somewhat greater in the ASP subjects. No information about two-point threshold in retardates has been found in the literature.

Ataxiometry. There seems to be a scant amount of information in the literature with which to compare the data from the ASP. Static ataxia for around 1000 normal subjects in the age range from 3 to 70 years was recorded by Edwards (1942). Both with eyes open and closed, he found a decrease in sway with age to about 20 years. He also reported the results for 100 feebleminded subjects, but no particulars, not even age or IQ, were given. It seems clear, however, that those retarded subjects had increased sway since the mean and *SD* of the group corresponded to the data of 4 year old normal subjects. The present data showed also development with age but not a clear deficiency in the retarded samples. Miles (1950) made the summary statement that although children are shorter than adults, it has usually been found that they sway more than adults. Witkin and Wapner (1950), using a recording method comparable to ASP's, but recording sum of head and hip sway in the two planes on 73 blindfolded college students, found that the women were significantly more steady than men. No such sex difference has been observed in the present data.

Strength of Grip. The relationship between strength of grip and development has been the concern of psychologists since the turn of the century and a considerable amount of information is available about this function. There is general agreement that strength continues to increase at least up to the age of 18, that right hand is stronger than left hand and that boys are stronger than girls (Smedley, quoted from Whipple, 1914; Baldwin, 1921; Woolley, 1926; Meredith, 1935; Jones, 1949; Francis & Rarick, 1960). There is considerably less agreement, however, with regard to absolute strength at the various age levels. Jones (1949) reviewed some of the earlier studies and found a tendency for the more recent studies to give higher scores than the earlier for corresponding age groups. His own results showed higher scores than any previously reported. This may or may not have been related to the fact that, while most of the other investigators used a Smedley Dynamometer, Jones did not.

Metheny (1941) summarized the findings of previous studies on strength of grip. She pointed out that such a measure depends primarily on two factors: the muscular strength and the willingness to exert this strength in the test situation. She concluded that "norms" do not exist for elementary school children because of differences in technique procedure, and age grouping. Comparing the data given for the Smedley Dynamometer, the normal sample of the ASP was within the range of the previous studies but close to the lower limit.

Distefano, Ellis, and Sloan (1958) recorded grip for a group of retarded subjects with mean CA of 19.7 for the males and 22.3 for the females. The scores were 32.3 and 23.8 kg respectively, which is remarkably close to the result for our oldest retarded samples (males 33.5, females 22.8 kg).

The data from the ASP are in agreement with previous studies on normal subjects with regard to age, sex, and laterality differences. We may therefore conclude that all three retarded samples of the ASP were decidedly below the level reached by normals of corresponding age. To illustrate this point we have expressed the ASP data as percentage of the norms given by Smedley. These data are presented in Table 14. The reason for using Smedley's data as reference is that the results from the ASP normal sample were in close agreement with his, and that he had age norms up to the age of 22. Thus the retardates seem not only to be late developers in this area, but to remain below the normal level.

Lower Arm Movement. This task was designed to record a simple motor task initiated by the subject himself, and it was expected that the retardates would perform relatively well. As it turned out, these were among the lowest scores for all three retarded samples. The literature does not contain data for retardates on a very similar task, but some of the problems will be discussed under the heading "Complexity of Motor Tasks."

Tapping. It is difficult to compare the ASP results on the Tapping test with previous investigations because methods have differed with regard to the dimensions of the tapping board, time interval for each trial, the number of trials, and prior practice. King (1954) used a tapping board similar to the ASP's, with ten 5 sec. trials (as compared to our 3 sec. trials) after 15 practice trials. Since he found only moderate practice effect, there is basis for a gross comparison. His 20-29 year old normal subjects had an average of 24 taps per 5 sec. trial. Since this is more than twice the 10.4 mean score obtained in 3 sec. for the ASP normals, there is indication that the function measured by this test was not matured in the 8-10 year old normal subjects who participated in the ASP.

The general conclusion of maximal performance's being reached in the late teens is substantiated by the results of earlier investigators who used "vertical" tapping in one spot rather than the oscillating

TABLE 14

STRENGTH OF GRIP SCORES FOR THE FOUR ABILITY STRUCTURE PROJECT SAMPLES EXPRESSED AS PERCENTAGE OF SMEDLEY'S AGE NORMS

		Sample 1	*Sample 2*	*Sample 3*	*Sample 4*
Males	R Hand	67	77	67	96
	L Hand	65	77	66	95
Females	R Hand	66	77	69	99
	L Hand	59	76	67	94

tapping used by King and in the ASP. Gilbert (1894, 1897) reported gradual increase of performance up to the age of 19, Smedley's data, as reported by Whipple (1914), indicated improvement up to the age of 16-18, and Woolley (1926) found a slight increase up to the age of 18. In a more recent study by Csank and Lehman (1958) which utilized finger tapping on a telegraph key, increase in score was reported from 5 to 20-25 years.

All the cited studies showed better performance by the males but the difference did not reach significance. This is in contrast to the ASP finding of faster tapping rate for the females than for the males in Samples 1, 3, and 4, reaching the 5% level of significance in the latter two groups. In several measures in the ASP study, the females performed better than the males—particularly in the normal sample, where previous studies had found males to perform better. This may indicate a more select group of females than males in the ASP samples.

The retarded samples in the present study did not reach the level of the 8-10 year old normals, in spite of the fact that the function does not seem to mature until the late teens. It appears, therefore, to be a function which is substantially depressed in mentally retarded subjects in general; suggesting deficiency rather than retardation.

Reaction Time. With a normal population, studies of Simple RT to light and sound are in agreement on the two following points: (a) RT decreases with maturation, and (b) boys are generally faster than girls, though the difference is usually not significant for the younger age groups (Gilbert, 1894; Bellis, 1933; Goodenough, 1935; Atwell & Elbel, 1948; and Csank & Lehman, 1958). The age level at which the fastest performance is found is variously given from 17 to college age. It appears from these studies that ASP's oldest retarded samples did not approach the normal performance level, but remained behind normal subjects of comparable age. It would appear that the retardates had RTs which were approximately 1½ to 2 times that of the normals. Except for the oldest retarded sample, boys had faster reaction time than girls.

A specific comparison of the RT results of the ASP group with previous results is somewhat difficult, because the age ranges do not match, but in general the agreement is very close. For auditory RT 209 ms were found for boys and 226 for girls. For 8-9 year olds, Goodenough reported 218 and 202 ms respectively, while Csank and Lehman found 205 ms for boys and 200 ms for girls in the age range from 5 to 9.

It is often stated that retardates have longer RT than normals, but data that have direct bearing on this question are not easy to find. There are several studies which have investigated reaction time in a mentally retarded population, but most often they were concerned with relationship between RT and MA or IQ or comparison of etiological groups. Sometimes the procedure has differed from the standard RT experiment, so that if data for normals were not included, it was difficult to make direct comparison. Scott (1940) compared 51 high IQ (120-200) children to 49 low IQ (63-94) children of the same CA for four RT tasks which varied in complexity with regard to stimulus and response. He found the high IQ boys and girls to be faster than low IQ boys and girls. Differences were more pronounced for the complex than for the simpler tasks. Sex difference was found among the high IQ groups but not among the low IQ groups. A study of Ellis and Sloan (1957 a) reported a mean RT to an auditory stimulus in 79 mentally retarded subjects in the age range from 10.3 to 19.5 to be 220 ms. This compares favorably to ASP's value of 241 ms for the 12-15 year old retarded sample.

Tizard and Venables (1956) found longer RT for a group of high grade retardates than for normals. These groups, however, differed in age; the retardates had a range of 16-21 years as compared to about 25-35 for the normals.

Using four RT tasks, Berkson (1960 b, 1960 c) concluded that the retardates were slower than normals on all measures utilized. His Simple Response Task was essentially the same as ASP's Simple Visual RT, and the results were quite similar.

In discussing her data from normal subjects, Goodenough (1935) referred to Luria, who has suggested that the development of the reaction process during childhood is shown, not merely by an improved speed of reaction, but, to an even more marked degree, in the gaining of voluntary control of the motor act. The improvement in voluntary control is shown in the gradual reduction of useless accessory movements preceding and accompanying the act of pressing the reaction key, and in fewer signs of bodily tension as age advances. This aspect of development seems to have greater consequences for variability than for the average speed. According to Luria's observation, the longer RT in the retardates could be due to deficiency of voluntary control of the motor act. If this were the case one would expect the difference between the normals and the retardates to be increased with increased complexity of the motor task. This relationship was not found in the ASP, and it may therefore be concluded that the present findings do not support this explanation of the longer RT in the retardates.

Berkson (1960 b) studied RTs with varying degree of response complexity and stimulus complexity in 16 familial retardates and 15 normal adolescent boys. In comparing hand lifting and button pressing to hand lifting alone, no interaction between IQ and task was found. In comparing response to single light with choice response to five lights, no interaction between IQ and task was found. From this he concluded that the difference in RT between the two groups is not accounted for by difference in speed of planning a movement or by difference in speed of scanning and making a choice. Difference in RT may be due to factors common to the tasks; i.e., speed in initiating the execution of a movement.

In a subsequent study, Berkson (1960 c) used the same RT tasks with five subject groups varying from normal to severely subnormal. The conclusions from the previous study were confirmed. Furthermore, it was indicated that speed of performing a movement was related to IQ, although from the study it was not possible to determine which response processes are related to IQ. Since the severely subnormal and mongoloids, matched for IQ, showed significant difference in RT, there was indication that other clinical variables than IQ are related to RT. ASP results have shown a moderate relationship between RTs and IQ for the retardates but not for the normals. If one compares RT and other motor measures which depend upon initiation, with Tapping–in which the factor of initiation does not enter–Berkson's interpretation of the role of initiation seems confirmed.

Data for Auditory Choice RT and Scrambled Foreperiod RT on retarded subjects has not been found in the literature.

Hand Precision. This test was scored for Hits and Errors separately. While the combination of the scores represents somewhat of a problem, the relationship between Hits and Errors was interpreted to represent task attitude and the overall level of the two measures (mean of *T* scores) to represent motor efficiency involving large muscles. Age norms or data for retarded populations have not been found in the literature. Ellis and Sloan (1957 b) studied rotary pursuit performance in relation to MA in retardates, a task which is rather similar to Hand Precision. They found a significant positive correlation (r=.43) which corresponds reasonably well to correlation coefficients for the retardates between Hand Precision Hits and Errors, on the one side, and Porteus and PMA-MA, on the other.

Purdue Pegboard. No significant sex differences were found in the Ability Structure Project data with regard to this test. This is in agreement with Eyman, Dingman, and Windle's (1959) report of a correlation of 0.00 between R + L + B and sex for 166 mentally retarded subjects. It seems obvious from Tobias and Gorelick's (1960) data that no sex difference existed among their 81 retarded adults.

The norms published by Tiffin and Asher (1948) for male industrial applicants were considerably higher than were the ASP scores for normal or retarded subjects. Thus it appears that the function measured by this test continues to develop beyond the age of 10. Siegel and Hirschborn (1958) presented data for 100 male adolescents in the age range of 12 to 18 years. From their data which concern subjects rather close to normal adults, they concluded: "Until more complete norms are furnished, it appears feasible to use existing published norms on the Purdue Pegboard with adolescents, and particularly with those above the age of 15." In view of this conclusion, it would appear from the ASP data that there is a rapid development in manual dexterity between the ages of 10 and 15. This is paralleled by the considerable difference in score between the 8-10 and 12-15 year old retardates, and means that if the two older retarded groups had been compared with normals of their own age range, they would probably have been as much below normal standard as were the 8-10 year olds.

This conclusion is strongly supported by the findings of Tobias and Gorelick (1960), who administered the Purdue Pegboard to 81 noninstitutionalized retarded adults with a mean IQ (WAIS) of 63 and a range of 35 to 78. All subjects were above 17 years of age. The following scores were found for males: R 39, L 39, B 29; and for females: R 40, L 39, B 31, which is in very close agreement with the ASP data for the two oldest retarded samples. These authors also pointed out that there is a significant difference in performance between the highest levels of a retarded population and the average industrial applicant.

There is also general agreement between the ASP results and the findings presented by Cantor and Stacey (1951) who administered the Purdue Pegboard to 175 mentally defective males ranging in age from 14 to 18 years and in IQ from 42 to 82. They found that ". . . . the defectives as a group and the 52 defectives making up the highest IQ level in the group (IQs 70-82) failed to compare favorably with the normal groups in terms of Pegboard scores." Furthermore, they found no significant differences among the various age levels in the defective population (14, 15, 16, 17, and 18 year olds) and concluded that in these individuals manual dexterity had reached maturity at the age of 14. In this aspect the retardates were not then different from the normals. Cantor and Stacey also found marked inability in manual dexterity in individuals with IQ below 60, but a great deal of overlap indicated that some individual defectives are capable of performing routine motor tasks on the normal level.

Again it is seen that Purdue Pegboard, similar to other measures in the battery, tapped a function which is substantially deficient rather than merely retarded.

Mirror Drawing. In reviewing the early literature on Mirror Drawing, Whipple (1915) stated that in all but two published reports women had a better time score than men. While the same tendency was found in the three retarded samples of the present study, the trend was reversed in the normal sample, a finding which is difficult to explain. These sex differences reached significant proportions in the oldest retarded and in the normal samples. Adequate age norms do not seem to exist for Mirror Drawing, but Clinton (1930), using numbers to be connected by pencil rather than the star pattern, found that both boys and girls improved continuously up to age 17, the age of the oldest group of his population.

Ellis, Barnett, and Pryer (1957) administered the Mirror Drawing task to 117 male and 53 female institutionalized mental defectives. Since they used the paper and pencil version of the test, the results are not directly comparable. It is, however, relevant that they found no sex difference in total time for ten massed trials. Of interest also is that only 54 subjects out of 170 were able to complete the tracing of the first star in 20 min. This would indicate that the tracing of the star-shaped groove with an automatic scoring procedure has a greater application and permits the use of the test with a greater variety of retardates. This difference in method was also reflected in the tracing time found by the two studies: a total time of 25-27 min. for 10 tracings in Ellis' study, as compared with a mean time score of 60-75 sec. (total time 10-12.5 min. for ten tracings) in the ASP study.

It is indeed puzzling that the performance level of the retardates was so close to the normal sample. The test scores did not follow the general trend of motor tasks. It seems difficult to assume that the motivational factors accounted for the level of the retardates, particularly in view of interpretation of such tasks as pure tone threshold and Lower Arm Movement. More feasible is the possibility that eye-hand coordination was not well established in the retardates and therefore interfered little with establishment of new coordinations. While these considerations make the test interesting for other purposes, it is a candidate for exclusion in the present connection, since it failed to differentiate between the four samples.

The Railwalking Test. Norms for boys and girls in the age range from 6 to 14 years have been presented by Heath (1949). His data showed that performance on this task improved gradually, at least up to the age of 14, and indicated no sex differences, at least up to the age of 12. ASP data also showed no significant sex differences in any of the samples; moreover, the improvement from Sample 1 to Sample 2 paralleled the trends in the normals. In a recent re-evaluation of Heath's norms, Goetzinger (1961) examined ninety boys and ninety girls in the age range 8-16. When the data were compared to Heath's norms, no significant differences were found. Goetzinger's data indicated increase in score until the age of 16, and, while the girls normally had a lower group mean, sex difference was apparently not significant.

Tizard (1950) found a mean of 82.9 when he administered the Railwalking test to 104 high grade adult retarded males. The generally higher level of his subjects (IQ about 75) may easily explain the difference between his findings and the ASP results on Railwalking (54.3). Distefano, Ellis, and Sloan (1958) included the Railwalking test in their study on motor proficiency in retardates. Their subjects covered an age range of ca. 20 years with a mean of 19.7 for the males and 22.3 for the females. The mean Railwalking score for these groups was 93.0 and 76.2 respectively. This is also a decidedly higher score than has been found in the Ability Structure Project. Even if difference in age range be considered, there is clear discrepancy between Distefano's findings and ASP's. In accounting for differences with Heath's findings, the authors suggested that ". . . perhaps the present findings are confounded by failure to differentiate clinical etiology." Heath (1942), who designed this test, used primarily as a tool to support etiological classification through test performance. He warned that mental deficiency should not be treated as an entity. He felt that it was necessary to show proper concern for etiological types if misleading results were to be avoided. In a later section of this presentation this problem will be discussed more fully. It is remarkable that in spite of the fact that maturation of this function is not reached until after 16 years of age, none of ASP's retarded samples reached the level of the 8-10 year old normals. The function measured by this test seems to be profoundly deficient in retardates.

Complexity of Motor Tasks. Several authors (Doll, 1933; Tredgold, 1947; Tizard, O'Connor, and Crawford, 1950) have noted more frequent occurrence of motor disturbance in retardates than in normals, but Doll observed that there was no significant correlation between level of intelligence and the severity of motor impairment. Also of interest is the following quotation from Clarke and Clarke (1958, p. 289): "It has been suggested that there is a close relationship between motor co-ordination and the general maturation process . . ." The importance of motor functions in psychiatric patients has been extensively investigated by King (1954).

It has generally been assumed that mentally retarded subjects are relatively more handicapped on complex tasks than on simple tasks. Such point of view has considerable common sense appeal. Werner (i.e., Werner & Thurma, 1942 b) has expressed the opinion that brain injured children have impaired cortical integration. This would certainly suggest, that for this etiological classification, increased complexity—either on stimulus or response side—would result in decreased motor efficiency. The findings of the ASP to the opposite effect were therefore not expected. While there seems to have been relatively little experimental investigation on this problem, there are a few studies which have reported a similar finding. Blackburn and Benton (1955) compared brain injured patients with a control group of neurological patients showing no evidence of cerebral disease and trauma. The brain injured group showed impairment in motor functions, 46% retardation for simple reaction time and 24% for choice reaction time. These investigators concluded that the simple motor function seems to discriminate more effectively between the two groups. In a subsequent study, Benton, Jentsch, and Wahler (1959) found a similar result by comparing schizophrenic and normal subjects. In a review article, King (1965 b) observed a reduction of psychomotor efficiency among diagnostic groupings of psychopathology and brain damage. The pattern of psychomotor performance seems to show a relatively greater loss for simple motor measures than for complex measures.

Other investigators have found an inverse relationship between task complexity and performance level. Scott (1940) compared 51 high IQ (120-200) children to 49 low IQ (63-94) children of the same age for 6 reaction time tasks of varying complexity. He found that the difference between the groups was less marked in the simplest test than in those in which several potential stimuli were used. The less intelligent defectives, according to Cantor and Stacey (1951), did fairly well on the simpler operations on the Purdue Pegboard (each hand separately) when compared to the defective group as a whole, but showed more deficiency for the more complex operations (both hands and assembly). The Oseretsky test was administered by Sloan (1951) to

20 normal and 20 retarded children, 10 of whom were classified as familials and 10 as undifferentiated. From the data he concluded: "It appears that degree of difficulty varies directly with the complexity of the task."

Fait and Kupferer (1956) studied motor achievement in retardates with vertical jump and the Burpee Squat Thrust. The concluded that the retardates are able to do the simpler task fairly well, but are less successful in the more complicated task.

Simple and discriminatory reaction times were recorded by Bensberg and Cantor (1957) on organic and familial subjects, with the expectation of obtaining a significant interaction between etiology and type of task. They found that the difference between organics and familials was greater on the discriminatory task than on the simple task. When the organics were divided into a group of "clear cut" and a group of questionable etiology, it was found that the "clear cut" group was still significantly slower than the familials on the speed measures, but the interaction was no longer significant. The authors concluded that the ambiguity of these findings is a result of the heterogeneity of the brain injured group.

From Hull's drive theory, Foshee (1958) deducted that increased amount of drive will have differential effects on performance in simple and in complex learning. Activity, as measured by a ballistocardiograph-like device, was used as an indication of drive, while card sorting of high and low complexity was the task. The predicted interaction was not significant.

Berkson (1960 b) compared 16 familial mentally deficient and 15 normal adolescent boys on three visual reaction time tasks of varying complexity. In his analysis of variance design, he found no significant interaction between task and IQ, which indicates that the normals were uniformly superior over the three tasks. In a subsequent study, Berkson (1960 c) compared four groups of defectives and one group of normals on two pairs of visual reaction time tasks which varied in stimulus complexity or response complexity. With regard to the interaction between groups and tasks he summarized the findings in the following way: "In the tasks in which the number of lights was changed, but the required response kept the same, no interaction of IQ and task was observed. A significant interaction was obtained between IQ and tasks in which the stimulus was held constant and the complexity of the required response was varied." Thus it appears that Berkson has gone a step further than the previous studies, in that he has shown that it is the response complexity rather than stimulus complexity which is a particular problem for the retardates.

Most of the studies appear to have demonstrated an inverse relationship between complexity of task—i.e., response complexity—and performance level. It is difficult to reconcile this with the findings of Blackburn and Benton, King, and the present author; i.e., lower performance on tasks with less response complexity. The possibility exists that these opposing results are due to the existence of a U-shaped function between task complexity and performance. It may also be that expressing the data of the retardates in terms of the mean and *SD* of the normals, as has been done in the present study, facilitates the comparison of simple and complex motor tasks.

If the perceptual tests are now considered, the first two to be discussed constitute a transition between motor and perceptual functions. Both *Word Association* and *RT to Pictures* concern speed of verbal production. The two measures showed considerable similarity in level for the three retarded samples, with significant difference from the normals. From the significant differences between Samples 1 and 2 it appeared that this function had not reached its maximum in the 8-10 year old retarded subjects. Neither age norms nor performance level data for retardates have been found in the literature regarding these functions; and our selection of purely neutral words prevents a comparison to standard clinical findings.

Span of Apprehension. Age norms for this function do not seem to be available. Sex differences have not been emphasized, hence there is no reason to assume that they exist. Thus there seems to be no contradiction with the finding in the ASP samples of no significant sex difference.

In a summary statement, Woodworth (1938, p. 690) says: "... when the objects are distinct black dots scattered irregularly over a white card and exposed to clear central vision for a period of from 37 to 100 ms (in the different experiments), the average span for keen adults is about 8." On a limited population (2 subjects) Hunter and Sigler (1940) found the maximum span to be 9 dots at exposure intervals of 150 ms. Considering that the exposure time in our experiment was 200 ms, and that our normal group was not limited to "keen" individuals, it would appear that this function is not fully matured (M = 5.6) at the age of 8-10. It may, however, approach maximum value at this age. Thus the difference in score between the youngest (3.7) and the oldest retarded samples (4.8 and 4.5) may be regarded as a normal growth increment, and it may be considered that our retarded subjects above the age of 10 showed a relatively constant reduction in span of apprehension in comparison with normals of the same chronological age.

Identification Threshold. Berkson (1960 a) used a technique which is similar to our Identification Threshold task. He determined the length of time a stimulus must be exposed in order to be correctly identified. Comparing normal and familial mentally-deficient boys, he found no significant differences between the two groups and concluded that duration threshold is not a factor which differentiates them.

While it is difficult to accept that duration threshold does not differentiate between retardates and normals, the present findings are in full agreement with those of Berkson. The mean performance level for this task in retardates is about 1½ *SD* below the normals. This difference does not reach significance because of a relatively large variability among the retardates. Such a spread in variability may suggest that the demand on attention and alertness by this test is an intermediate one. Those who can rally their attention when a certain pressure is asserted will have close to normal score. For those where the attention function is more disturbed the performance level will suffer, resulting in greater variability.

Recognition of Non-meaningful Material. This is another test for which the material was prepared relative to needs of this study and consequently there are no data with which to compare the present findings; nor have norms or data concerning retardates been found regarding any similar task.

Azimuth. The two variables recorded in this test correlated more highly among the retardates (from .57 to .66) than within the normal sample (.32). Both variables showed significant differences between the normals and each of the three retarded samples. Azimuth Reversal showed the unusual feature of a lower score for the oldest than for the youngest retarded sample. No data from other normal or retarded populations seem available.

Brightness Discrimination. Contrary to expectation, this variable did not discriminate between retardates and normals. It is one of the very few variables where all three retarded samples had better scores than had the normals. The reason for this is not easy to understand. It may be related to the lack of standard dark adaptation prior to the test, but the consistency of the three retarded samples does not support this. Age norms or data for retardates have not been encountered in the literature. It is interesting to remember that Lashley (1929) found impairment of maze learning but not of brightness discrimination in rats with cortical injuries.

CFF. ASP data showed significant sex differences for Samples 1, 2, and 4 but not for Sample 3. In all four samples, however, CFF was higher for boys than for girls. The finding of significant sex differences is in agreement with Miller (1942) but not with Misiak (1947, 1951). With regard to relationship between CFF and age, most investigators of this problem have been concerned with the decrease of CFF as a function of old age. Our particular problem is whether CFF is expected to increase beyond the age of our control sample. In comparing 38 children in the age range 5 to 12 years with 22 adults, Meili and Tobler (1931) found no difference between these groups when CFF was determined by a rotating sector disc. In comparing 6-11 year old subjects with 18-25 year olds, Hartmann (1934) found no difference. Simonson, Enzer, and Blankstein (1941) have published data for two groups, 10-19 and 20-29. The difference between means was .3 cps—obviously not significant—but the *N* was so small that the finding does not carry much weight. Miller (1942) concluded from his study of 77 subjects in the age range from 6 to 18 that: "The results . . . do not disclose a definite trend in the direction of an increase in the critical frequency limen for visual flicker corresponding to an increase in chronological age." Misiak's (1951) data might suggest subjects in the 12-16 range to have higher CFF than subjects in the 7-11 or 16-21 range, but the differences do not appear to be significant. The data of Csank and Lehman (1958) may be interpreted to mean that no increase in CFF should be expected beyond the 8-10 year age level. McFarland, Warren, and Karis (1958) concluded that the relationship between CFF and age was linear and negative for ten light-dark ratios used under two conditions of surround luminance. Of particular interest is the fact that the 13-19 year old group had higher CFF thresholds than the 20-29 year old group for all light-dark ratios.

Because of difference in testing procedures, brightness, light-dark ratios, visual angle, etc., comparison to actual thresholds found in these studies is without interest.

Although none of the cited studies included a substantial number of subjects in the young age range, there was sufficient agreement among them to indicate that CFF is a function which matures rather early, and that it has reached its highest level at the age of 10. With regard to the CFF in ASP's retarded subjects we may conclude that the maximum level is reached at the same age as is characteristic for the normals but that this level is 3-4 cycles below that of the normals.

In comparing retarded subjects with evidence of brain injury, with retarded children without such evidence, Werner and Thuma (1942 b) found lower CFF for the brain injured subjects for three brightness levels. Mark, Meier, and Pasamanick (1958) compared 10 children with pyramidal tract brain damage with 10 non-brain injured children of comparable sex, age, and IQ distribution. Both foveal and peripheral CFF were lower for the brain-injured group, but only the peripheral measure reached significance. These two studies indicated that the brain injury or its consequences, rather than the retarded state, caused the lowered CFF.

Stereognosis. In spite of the fact that this test had a rather low reliability coefficient, the significance of the function is suggested in the correlation analysis. Only the youngest and oldest retarded samples differed significantly from the normals. The three retarded samples did not differ from each other, even though the difference between the means of the 8-10 and 12-15 samples was greater than for any other perceptual variable. Age norms or data for retardates on stereognosis do not seem to be available.

Time Interval Estimation. This variable is not a powerful discriminator between normals and retardates, since only the oldest retarded sample differed significantly from the normals. The mean of each of three retarded samples was within one standard deviation from the normals. This measure has apparently not been used for a retarded population before, and age norms for normals are not reported in the literature. Both retardates and normals in the present study underestimated the 5 sec. interval; the normals more than the retardates.

Weight Lifting. Gilbert (1894) found that the weight-size illusion is well developed at the age of six, increases gradually to age nine, and then declines slowly with age. Consequently this function should have been fully developed in our normal sample. All of our retarded samples showed less weight-size illusion than did the normals. It appears that our retardates continued to develop to the age of 12-15, and that, even at that age, they had not reached the level of the normals. Why retardates showed less susceptibility to the illusion than normals is difficult to understand, unless it reflected less experience in contact with and manipulation of the outside world. According to Piaget, weight-size illusion is a secondary illusion which develops with age in the normal child. It is the result of what he calls "perceptual activities" and "semireversibility." The latter term refers to a compromise situation between perception and thought (Berlyne, 1957).

Charpentier's illusion, where weight is constant while size varies, has been used by Ohwaki (1953). He found that the illusion is seldom experienced below the age of four, but develops rapidly between four and five years of age. The development of illusion is also delayed in retarded children and found to be related to MA rather than CA. He contributed the development of the illusion to two factors: (a.) integral differentiation between pressure sensation and vision, and (b.)

lack of experience which would indicate the relationship between size and weight. Thus Ohwaki also reached the conclusion that ". . . integral differentiation of specific function is impaired or delayed in the retardates . . ."

Jenkin and West (1958) found that brain damaged subjects were significantly less susceptible to the weight-size illusion than were normal subjects. A direct comparison between organic and normal subjects has not been made in the present study. The youngest retarded were significantly different from the normals, but the organics did not differ significantly from the other etiological categories. Indications are that the Ability Structure Project supports Jenkin and West in their finding, but extends it to other etiological categories as well.

Muller-Lyer Illusion. The magnitude of illusion created by the Muller-Lyer figures depends on a number of factors, such as length of the standard and the obtuseness of the arrow heads and their length. It is therefore futile to make direct comparisons of ASP results with those of other investigators. An effort was made in this project to achieve sizeable illusions and thus the dimensions of the Muller-Lyer figures were longer than any previously described. It is consistent with this that the magnitude of illusion is greater than that generally reported in the literature (see review of Walters, 1942).

In agreement with earlier studies, the data did not show a sex difference. Therefore, primary concern is with the relationship between illusion and age. Pintner and Anderson (1916) measured illusion on 250 children in the 6-14 age range, and on 28 adults. When "inwards" and "outwards" judgements were averaged, the data showed a slight tendency toward decrease of illusion and better attention in the older subjects. Thirteen feeble-minded subjects, all with MA of 9, did not seem to differ from the normals. Walters (1942) tested 1700 subjects in the age range from 6 to 19. Her own conclusion (p. 143) was: ". . . the mean illusion decreases with increasing age up to 11 years. It seems probable that 11 years is the age at which maturity in this function is reached." Her data indicated that for males the illusion continues to decrease up to age 17, while a reversal takes place in the females from 11 to 17. This reversal is explained as a result of a refusal of the older girls to become "involved" in the task. ASP indicated a slight decrease with age for both males and females. As a consequence, the two older retarded samples had scores for Muller-Lyer Extent which may have been closer to their age norms than Fig. 3 would indicate, since normals of comparable age would also be less susceptible to the illusion. The difference in extent of illusion, however, did not reach significance for any of the ASP samples.

The conclusions of Pinter and Anderson, and Walters, have been conrmed by Wapner and Werner (1957), who also found a decrease in the Muller-Lyer illusion in the age range 6 to 12.

Jenkin and West (1959) found that brain damaged subjects were somewhat less susceptible to the illusion than were normal subjects. Since the two groups differed substantially in difference between "inward" and "outward" judgements (anticipation), the authors sugested that general insensitivity of discrimination, rather than optical illusion per se, may have accounted for the findings. The present study did not support either of these findings. Spitz and Blackman (1958) reported less of an illusion in 24 high grade retarded boys than in 22 normal boys, but the difference was not significant. They related their findings to satiation and suggested that the initial phase of the satiation process is to some extent responsible for the perception of the illusion.

In agreement with the present findings these studies have all reported a tendency of the retardates to have perceived less Muller-Lyer illusion than did normals, even though the difference does not reach significant proportions.

Complex Mental Measures. Tobias and Gorelick (1962) administered the Porteus Mazes to more than 200 non-institutionalized retarded adults. The mean Maze score (MA) was 8.4 and the mean full scale WAIS IQ 60.2. The Maze score corresponded closely to the results of ASP's two older samples, 8.2 and 7.9 respectively. As their PMA-IQ scores were 51.2 and 48.6, this seems to confirm a previously mentioned notion that the PMA scores in retardates tend to be depressed.

The Raven scores for the four samples were 13.7, 21.0, 20.1, and 33.0 respectively, indicating a significant difference between the normal and all three retarded samples. Comparing a control group with a group of brain damaged subjects (cerebro-vascular accident), Urmer, Morris, and Wendland (1960) found that the latter group performed in a poorer fashion qualitatively as well as quantitatively.

Comparison of IQ in the present and previous studies is not particularly meaningful, since difference in results primarily reflects difference in sampling.

Summary

This literature review has concerned the following three problems: (a.) Agreement between ASP data and other reports on comparable measures for retardates and normals; (b.) Agreement regarding sex differences in the present and previous studies; and (c.) Indication of developmental trends for the measures included in the ASP. The coverage of the problems is spotty, since the literature does not seem to supply the relevant information for many of the variables used in the present study. In comparisons of this type, proper allowance has to be made for differences in technique and sampling procedures.

On such basis, the data for the ASP retardates are in most cases in agreement with previous findings for retardates. It appears that the ASP values for Railwalking are somewhat lower than those found by Tizard et al. (1950) and Distefano et al. (1958). Also, several authors have reported a direct relationship between performance level and task complexity, whereas the opposite relationship, found in the present study, is supported only by two studies. In view of the three independent samples; the large *N* in each of them; the large number of motor variables; and the transformation to standard scores for more adequate comparison, the present findings carry considerable weight.

The lack of sex difference found in the present study is in most instances supported by previous studies. Discrepancies are found for Ataxiometry, where Witkin and Wapner (1950) found differences; for Tapping, where the ASP showed faster tapping rate for the females as compared to the reverse finding by other authors; and for CFF, where we are in agreement with Miller (1942), but not with Misiak (1951).

Developmental trends in normals have primarily been established for motor functions. There is rather solid evidence to indicate that the older retarded samples for these functions were as much below their age norms as were the youngest retardates below the 8-10 year old normals. The same trend was indicated for Span of Apprehension and Weight Lifting. For most of the perceptual variables information is sparse. It is suggested, however, that perceptual functions mature before motor functions.

It may be concluded that, in general, the present data for retardates and for normals are representative for the respective populations.

NEUROLOGICAL SAMPLE

Three samples of subjects—matched for age, IQ, and male-female ratio, but varying in degree of neurological involvement—were selected for further analysis. It should be emphasized that this attempts a gross classification of degree of neurological manifestation rather than type of impairment. The data will at a later date be analyzed for type and locus of impairment. The three samples, each including 25 subjects, were: N1 without neurological signs, N2 with slight impairment, and N3 with severe neurological impairment. The definitions of slight and severe neurological impairment have been given in the section "The Neurological Examination."

The statistical analysis in comparing these samples was the same as had been used before: an overall analysis of variance was made (Table 7) and for those variables where the *F* ratio was significant at the 5% level, comparisons of means were made with *t* tests. Since this involved multiple comparison, the 1% level was used as criterion of significance. The variables where significance occurred are entered in Table 15. The table shows that different degrees of neurological involvement seemed to be of consequence for very few variables. In view of the number of comparisons made, the significant differences could have occurred by chance. There is, however, an internal consistency to the data of Table 15 which gives them some face value validity. Where differences occurred they were between Groups N1 and N3 or between Groups N2 and N3. This indicates that the marginal neurological involvement which constitutes the criterion for slight impairment does not manifest itself in the functions measured by our tests. As may be seen in the table, N3 always had poorer scores than the other samples, and the difference was substantial. It is worth noticing as a trend that N1 had consistently better scores than N2, even if these differences never reached significance.

Five of the six variables in Table 15 are motor measures; involving strength, fine finger coordination, and gross body movement. It appears that these variables require a high level of integration of the central nervous system which is impaired in subjects with definite

TABLE 15

GROUP MEANS (RAW SCORES) AND SIGNIFICANCE LEVEL (1%) FOR VARIABLES WHICH SHOW SIGNIFICANT DIFFERENCES BETWEEN MEANS IN THE NEUROLOGICAL SAMPLE

Variable	*Group N1*	*Group N2*	*Group N3*	*Significance* N1-N2	N1-N3	N2-N3
Eye Dom.	2.44	2.58	1.34			X
Grip L	24.70	21.73	16.56		X	
Pegboard R	37.04	36.12	28.68		X	X
Pegboard L	35.60	34.76	26.08		X	X
Pegboard B	28.96	27.00	19.76		X	X
Railwalking	45.20	43.24	19.68		X	X

neurological signs. There was noticeable mixed eye dominance in N1 and N2 and noticeable left eye dominance in N3. Grip L and Railwalking revealed the greatest difference between N1 and N2 and may have a potential power of discrimination between subjects without neurological sign and those with slight neurological impairment. The greater difference between N2 and N3 for Railwalking indicates that this measure is particularly sensitive to CNS impairment. The maintenance of balance while walking along a rail requires the integration of muscular action in all parts of the body; hence any CNS impairment will interfere with this task.

Our samples constituted somewhat of a selection, since individuals with gross motor, sensory, or language disturbance were excluded; i.e., individuals with profound neurological disturbance. Actually N3 might have been called moderately impaired. Our results indicate that for a wide variety of measures there is no deficiency of skills related to moderate neurological impairment. The measures which seemed to reflect such impairment were fine finger and gross body coordination, muscular strength, and eye dominance.

EEG SAMPLE

In a similar manner to that described for the Neurological Sample, three groups of retardates with varying degrees of EEG abnormality but matched for CA, IQ, and male-female ratio were selected. Again this was a gross grouping where the subjects were classified as those with normal (E1); those with borderline (E2); and those with abnormal EEG pattern (E3). Type or location of EEG abnormality was not considered here, but those data are in the process of analysis. Each subject group in this sample was comprised of 76 subjects, and the data were treated as described for other group comparisons. A complicating factor was that a number of individuals included had also neurological impairment. Of the 228 subjects, 60 were included in the neurological sample. As almost three-fourths of the EEG sample did not overlap with the neurological sample, the two samples were reasonably independent. The means of the variables which showed significant *F* ratio in the analysis of variance (Table 7) and the differences between means which reached the 1% significance level, are entered in Table 16.

On several points, these results are similar to what was found for the neurological sample. There are relatively few variables where EEG abnormality was reflected in performance level, even if there were about twice as many as were found for the neurological sample.

TABLE 16

GROUP MEANS (RAW SCORES) AND SIGNIFICANCE LEVEL (1%) FOR VARIABLES WHICH SHOW SIGNIFICANT DIFFERENCES BETWEEN MEANS IN THE EEG SAMPLE

Variable	*Group E1*	*Group E2*	*Group E3*	*Significance*		
				E1-E2	*E1-E3*	*E2-E3*
Grip R	26.16	22.65	18.75		X	
Scrambled RT	382.55	429.68	490.36		X	
Hand Prec. Err.	4.8	5.6	6.7		X	
Pegboard R	37.71	36.33	33.50		X	
Pegboard B	29.29	28.08	25.29		X	
Mirr. Dr. Err.	64.75	73.84	83.46		X	
Railwalking	53.22	49.18	36.55		X	X
Span of Appreh.	4.81	4.53	4.29		X	
Porteus M A	8.68	7.62	6.70		X	
Porteus I Q	67.12	59.72	55.16		X	

This may mean that abnormal EEG patterns are associated with more extensive performance impairment than is severe neurological impairment, as these terms are defined in the present study. With one exception, significant differences were found only between the extreme groups but not between adjacent groups. Another similarity is that there was a gradual decrease in performance level from Group E1 through Group E2 to Group E3.

The variables which discriminated between the groups in the neurological sample, with exception of Eye Dominance, also showed significant differences between the groups in the EEG sample. Thus individuals with abnormal EEG patterns were likely to show impairment of fine finger coordination and gross bodily movement. In addition, they had a narrower span of apprehension, less ability to sustain attention—as indicated by Scrambled RT—and poorer performance on the Porteus Maze Test. The Porteus Maze Test has been variously interpreted from time to time. The most adequate interpretation in the present connection may be "a measure of foresight and planning," which may also be related to a more narrow apprehension span.

Mirror Drawing Errors and Hand Precision Errors once more behaved in a similar fashion, with E3 having a greater error rate per unit of time or hits. Thus EEG abnormality was associated with impaired large-muscle coordination and integration of visual-motor cues. These measures are among the few tasks which develop with CA without reversal at the adult level, and seem to be affected by the disturbance of cortical integration, which is reflected in the abnormal EEG.

As was the case in the neurological sample, Railwalking—but not Ataxiometry—differentiated between the extreme categories of EEG abnormality. This is additional evidence of the independence of these two variables which would seem to be closely related; and again, the complex coordination of muscular activity in the entire body and the integration of visual-motor clues seemed to be the functions which were impaired. The sensitivity of this variable is indicated by the fact that it is the only variable which showed significant difference between the borderline and abnormal EEG.

It seems that individuals with abnormal EEG have a tendency to impaired span of apprehension; impaired level of sustained attention; and impairment of what has been called foresight and planning. These are in addition to the poorer performance on all levels of muscle coordination and strength of grip—which also seem to be interfered with in individuals with clear neurological signs. It seems indicated that positive neurological signs are related to motor performance, while EEG abnormality seems to be related to the more abstract integration as well. One's expectation of a retarded child's academic achievement may be influenced—not only by his IQ—but also by whether or not he has a normal EEG pattern.

The 8-15 per sec. spindles which Gibbs and Gibbs (1962) reported to have found in 17% of 300 non-institutionalized retarded children below the age of eight were not observed in the present study. There may be several reasons for this. The present retarded population was older than the one studied by Gibbs and Gibbs. Also, these authors observed that the spindles were particularly frequent in cerebral palsy and athetoid patients, and therefore seem to be associated with impairment of the extrapyramidal system. There is reason to believe that such cases had been screened out from the present population.

NEUROLOGICAL AND EEG SAMPLES

A group of subjects with both neurological impairment and EEG abnormality was selected as a supplement to the group comparison of the neurological and the EEG sample. The question was asked if greater behavioral decrement would be found in subjects having both types of impairment of the central nervous system. Such a combination would presumably give a more adequate appraisal of the severity of organic impairment. Using the same definition of neurological impairment and EEG abnormality as was discussed in the two previous sections, these four groups of retarded subjects were selected: Normal EEG and no neurological impairment (NE1); Borderline EEG and no or slight neurological impairment (NE2); Abnormal EEG and slight or no neurological impairment, or Normal or Borderline EEG and severe neurological impairment (NE3); and Abnormal EEG and severe neurological impairment (NE4). Each group contained 39 subjects and, as before, they were matched for age, IQ, and male-female ratio. Statistical analysis of the data is also identical to that for the overall samples.

Table 7 lists the *F* ratios and Table 17 shows the Means and indicates level of significance for those variables where significant differences between Means occurred. This table has been restricted to those combinations where differences were found, but all possible combinations have been considered. The data show several of the same characteristics which were found when neurological impairment and EEG abnormality were considered separately: few variables were found where the differences reached the 1% level; those found were between extreme groups, NE1 and NE4 or NE2 and NE4; and a general decline in performance was noted as we went from Group NE1 to Group NE4. With exception of Eye Dominance, all the variables which appeared in the neurological sample were again significant. Of the additional variables in the EEG sample, only Grip R and Porteus IQ appeared. A single variable, Speed of Tapping—which was not significant in the separate samples—reached significance level here where dual indication of brain damage was considered. This addition of only one variable makes one hesitate in attaching too much importance to it.

TABLE 17

GROUP MEANS (RAW SCORES) AND SIGNIFICANCE LEVEL (1%) FOR VARIABLES WHICH SHOW SIGNIFICANT DIFFERENCES BETWEEN MEANS IN THE NEURO-EEG SAMPLE

Variable	*NE1*	*NE2*	*NE3*	*NE4*	*Significance* *NE1-NE4*	*NE2-NE4*	*NE1-NE3*
Grip L	21.31	18.96	15.21	14.84	X		
Grip R	23.20	21.17	15.58	16.23	X		
Tapping	9.55	8.45	8.11	7.95	X		
Pegboard R	37.21	34.51	31.05	29.15	X	X	X
Pegboard L	36.18	32.95	30.62	28.10	X		X
Pegboard B	29.31	26.46	23.59	20.92	X	X	X
Railwalking	55.62	45.46	35.72	24.59	X	X	X
Porteus IQ	61.95	56.23	55.90	48.64	X		

Porteus MA, Span of Apprehension, Scrambled RT, Mirror Drawing Errors and Hand Precision Errors reached the level of significance in the EEG samples, but not in the present sample where neurological impairment as well as EEG patterns were considered. This finding may be interpreted in at least two different ways. One could argue that if the findings from the EEG sample were valid the same differences would show up in the present sample, since these groups also vary with regard to EEG pattern. The fact that several variables did not reach significance in the present sample might be interpreted as indicating that the previous finding is not substantiated by the present one.

Another interpretation would emphasize that neurological and EEG abnormality result in different types of functional impairment. Dividing the population into subgroups on the basis of combined neurological and EEG criteria might tend to cancel out differences previously found by introducing greater variance and conflicting trends. The combined groups seemed to involve primarily motor function found in the EEG and neurological subgroups.

Regardless of which of these interpretations one would favor, the original expectation of finding more extensive behavioral decrement by combining neurological and EEG indices has not been supported. One obtains as much, if not more, information on the subjects by considering these indices separately.

While EEG abnormality seemed to have more definite consequences for ability structure than had neurological impairment, these consequences were relatively minor. From brain pathology diagnosed through neurological signs and EEG, one cannot predict deficiency in a number of sensory, motor, perceptual, and complex mental functions. With the number of tests in our battery, this should be a fairly general conclusion. It appears that brain insult is not necessarily reflected in functional deficiencies; on the other hand one may find deficiencies of skills to exist without any indication of central nervous system impairment.

ETIOLOGICAL SAMPLE

Finally: an attempt was made to assess the importance of etiology for the performance level of the tests in the battery. For this purpose each retarded individual in the study was classified according to the Riggs and Rain system. As we have previously explained, this system allows for the following main categories: Familials, Organics, Unexplained, Mixed, Mongoloid and Non-classifiable. The retarded population was not equally distributed over these categories. Therefore, to get a reasonable number of subjects in each group, an initial comparison was limited to Familials, Organics, Unexplained and Mixed. Each group included 32 subjects, matched for age, IQ, MA, and male-female ratio. The data were analyzed by the same statistical procedure as the group comparisons above. Table 7 shows the unexpected outcome of the analysis of variance for the 50 variables: only a single variable, CFF, reached significance at the 5% level. Thus we may conclude that except for CFF, etiological classification appears to be unrelated to performance level and fails to suggest the need for differentiation in training program.

Mean *T* score and *SD* of *T* scores were computed for the four etiological groups and the results were entered in Table 18. This table shows that overall ability and performance variability across the many tasks did not differ among the four etiological groups.

While other authors have also failed to find difference between etiological groups (see Survey of Literature elsewhere in this chapter), there are a number of studies in the literature which report such difference. Because of this background, the absolutely negative result of the present analysis was not expected. It was therefore decided to probe further into the data by analyzing the etiological categories for the total sample in each of the three age samples. In Table 19 are listed the *N*, CA, IQ, Mean *T* score, *T* score *SD*, and Male-Female ratio for these subgroups. While *N* and Male-Female ratio varied considerably in the various subgroups, the remaining four measures were remarkably constant for the subgroups within each age sample. There was a noticeable exception to this general rule: the mongoloids in the two oldest retarded samples had decidedly lower IQ, performance level and higher across-trait variability than had any of the other etiological groups. Analysis of variance gave significant *F* ratio for Mean of *T* score in the two oldest samples, and subsequent *t* tests indicated significant differences between several of the etiological subgroups. Closer inspection of this data showed that where significant

TABLE 18

MEAN *T* SCORE AND *SD* OF *T* SCORE IN THE FOUR ETIOLOGICAL CATEGORIES (N=32 IN EACH CATEGORY)

	Familials	*Organics*	*Unexplained*	*Mixed*
Mean	43.1	42.6	43.9	43.3
SD	17.6	16.6	18.6	16.5

TABLE 19

CA,IQ, MEAN *T* SCORE, *SD* OF *T* SCORE, AND MALE-FEMALE RATIO FOR ETIOLOGICAL SUBGROUPS IN EACH RETARDED AGE SAMPLE

		Familial	*Organic*	*Mixed*	*Unknown*	*Non-classif.*	*Mon-goloids*
8–10 Year Old	N	10	38	11	6	3	
	CA	113.6	114.8	113.9	119.5	108.3	
	IQ	56.6	58.2	54.9	55.7	60.3	
	Mean T	32.8	34.3	34.4	37.5	34.1	
	SD of T	22.6	21.7	22.9	22.4	26.6	
	M/F	4/6	29/9	9/2	6/0	3/0	
12–15 Year Old	N	14	42	27	10	8	4
	CA	170.9	165.6	165.4	167.9	183.4	173.5
	IQ	53.3	51.2	52.3	58.5	49.9	39.8
	Mean T	45.3	41.3	43.2	47.7	46.1	31.0
	SD of T	15.8	17.8	16.2	18.5	18.1	27.1
	M/F	11/3	30/12	12/15	8/2	5/3	3/1
20–24 Year Old	N	11	43	12	17	12	8
	CA	271.0	258.5	250.4	250.0	262.5	285.3
	IQ	56.7	46.7	48.6	54.4	49.1	35.1
	Mean T	46.9	38.1	41.2	45.0	42.9	32.1
	SD of T	16.4	22.8	19.1	17.2	18.0	25.2
	M/F	6/5	30/13	8/4	10/7	8/4	8/0

group differences occurred, the two groups differed in IQ and that the group with the higher IQ had invariably a higher Mean *T* score. Since high positive correlation has been found between Mean *T* score and IQ, it is likely that the significant group differences reflected differences in IQ, rather than genuine differences between etiological categories.

A considerable number of experimental studies in mental retardation have been concerned with comparisons between familials and organics, and many of these studies have reported significant differences between such groups on several variables. Too many comparisons of etiological groups exist in the literature to permit a complete survey, therefore only a few representative studies have been selected.

In a discussion about terminology, Stevens and Birch (1957) summarized the term "brain injured," used by Strauss in his early writing, as describing children with perceptual learning, thinking and personality disturbances. In such children there is a tendency to perseveration, hyperactivity, rigidity or stereotypy, motor disinhibition, and attention to details rather than wholes. This is contrasted to a quotation from Wortis: "There is . . . no brain-injured child, but only a variety of brain-injured children whose problems are quite varied and whose condition calls for far more refined analysis than some of the current generalizations on the brain-injured child provide." The relationship between CNS impairment and behavior, as well as terminology—for instance, the definition of brain injury—is far from clear.

This confusion accounts for many of the apparent inconsistencies noted below.

According to Werner and Strauss (1939) a global type of visuo-motor behavior is characteristic for the exogenous retardates, while an incoherent type is characteristic for the endogenous (familial-genetic) retardates. Global behavior represents an underdeveloped form for activity and may be interpreted in terms of genetic psychology, while incoherent behavior can only be interpreted in terms of pathology.

Since Strauss and Lehtinen (1947) regarded distractability as a characteristic of the organic retardate (exogenous), several authors have investigated this problem. Gardner, Cromwell, and Foshee (1959) measured activity by means of a "ballistograph" under conditions of visual stimulation (colored cloth, trinkets, and light on a screen) and reduced visual stimulation. When contrasting organics and familials, no difference in activity was found. A comparison of hyperactives with hypoactives revealed that there was a significantly greater discrepancy between conditions in the former group. These findings are interpreted as need for stimulation. Using similar visual conditions, Cromwell and Foshee (1960) recorded activity level (ballistograph) and card sorting performance. No differences were found as a function of visual stimulation or etiological classification (familial-organic). Similarly, Spradlin, Cromwell, and Foshee (1960) found that auditory stimulation failed to affect activity level or show difference between familial and organic subjects. In all three of these studies it was pointed out that the subjects were not selected according to Strauss' criteria.

Cruse (1961) recorded RT under different degrees of distraction and found that brain injured subjects with definite signs of organic injury were more distractable than familials. Familials, however, benefited as much as brain injured subjects from a minimum of environmental distraction. This finding may be interpreted as a difference between the two etiological groups in performance level rather than in distractability. Ellis, Hawkins, Pryer, and Jones (1963) pointed out that "Some of the studies which have tended to support Strauss' position have selected 'brain injured' Ss with behavioral criteria which were identical with or similar to the dependent behavior. Others have selected samples on the basis of highly tenuous case histories or equally unreliable 'neurological findings'."

Hunt and Patterson (1958) found that the familial group of retarded children performed better than brain injured children on tasks which involved visual and auditory cues. Many brain injured children would rely on one cue only, to the exclusion of the other.

In a comparison between mongoloids and familials, Berkson (1960 c) found a slower RT in the mongoloids, even with MA held constant. Similarly, Bensberg and Cantor (1957) reported significantly faster simple and discrimination RTs in familial than in organic subjects. Comparing undifferentiated and familial subjects with regard to Purdue Pegboard, Eyman et al. (1959) did not find significant differences. Endogenous and exogenous subjects, however, compared by Heath (1942) for Railwalking, showed a substantial difference. In another study of motor tasks, Pascal, Stolurow, Zabarenko, and Chambers (1951) used 27 male mental defectives, ranging in age from 6 to 32 years, and found no difference in score for delayed reaction between familials, undifferentiated, and organics, but their population was rather small for this type of comparison.

Endogenous and exogenous children were compared by Hoakley and Frazeur (1945) with respect to preception, visuo-motor activity, and thought organization as shown in their performance on the Binet scale. Their failure to demonstrate differences between the two samples seems to have puzzled the authors, who suggested that the negative findings may have been a result of a too small sample, heterogeneity of the sample, or lack of sensitivity in the task instrument.

Werner and Thuma (1942 a) compared a group of brain injured children with a group of endogenous children and found that the former group was defective in apparent motion perception, though they were able to perceive real motion. They experienced simultaneity at a slower rate of succession than the endogenous group, they rarely saw motion in tachistoscopically presented simple figures, and experienced less influence of one exposure on a following one. The authors concluded that the mechanisms of integration are impaired in the brain injured children, and quote Goldstein's interpretation—that cortical lesion interferes with interaction, resulting in relative isolation of neural events. In another study dealing with perceived motion, McMurray (1954) reported that brain injured mentally retarded children had fewer reversals in the perception of Lissajous figures than had familials.

Werner and Thuma (1942 b) found significantly lower CFF at three brightness levels for brain injured than for endogenous retarded children. They concluded that the CFF process is more central than peripheral, and regarded the findings as a result of impaired integration mechanism. It is the interpretation of these authors that relative isolation of neural events (in accordance with Goldstein's concept) may result in prolonged aftereffect, as a consequence of reduced inhibition from other centers. Thus fusion would occur at a slower flashing rate. In the present study CFF is the only measure where significant differences were found by comparing etiological categories. Since 50 variables were compared, however, the possibility of chance occurrence can not be entirely dismissed.

Familials, organics, and unexplained were compared with respect to social maturity by Cassel and Riggs (1953). Social age and Social quotient showed significant difference between Familials and Organics, while the Unexplained were not different from either. By exploring type of tasks involved, they found that tasks requiring visual motor coordination were more often failed by the organics. On this basis one might have expected many of the tasks in the present study to discriminate between these groups. The fact that they did not seems compelling evidence against the specific role of visual-motor coordination in organics.

Gallagher (1957) compared two matched groups of brain injured and familial retardates for an extensive battery of tests, including measures of perception, learning aptitude, intellectual scatter, language development, quantitative ability, and personality characteristics. He concluded that there are large areas of similarity between the two etiological groups, as well as some differences. The differences were particularly found for personality characteristics, the brain injured had less desirable characteristics than the familials.

Garrison (1958) reported on comparisons of three etiological groups of retarded subjects (familials, unexplained, and organics) for the following tests: Stanford-Binet, PMA, California Achievement Test, Porteus Mazes, H-T-P, the Vineland Social Maturity Scale, and Bender-Gestalt. No consistent differences between etiological groups were found.

Four etiological groups (undifferentiated familials, infectious traumatic, mongoloids, and miscellaneous diagnoses) were compared by Meyers, Dingman, Attwell, and Orpet (1961) by means of a 13 test battery designed to sample factors known to be well established in adults. The mongoloids differed from the others with respect to two variables; otherwise no difference was found.

The lack of difference between etiological subgroups reported in the last three studies also seems to be in accord with findings reported by Malamud (1954). On the basis of neuropathological findings in 543 autopsied cases of mental deficiency, he concluded that an etiological classification of these individuals is not warranted at the present stage of knowledge.

Some of the studies reviewed above have reported differences between etiological subgroups of retardates and others have not found such differences. An extreme in the latter direction is the present study, where, of 50 variables, only a single significant difference was found. Such divergencies can hardly be accounted for in terms of the tasks administered, for differences have been reported for CFF, Railwalking, simple and disjunctive reaction time, which are included in the ASP battery. It seems more likely that the discrepancies resulted from sampling procedures or from differences in defining the terms organic and brain injured. There is little doubt that the extent of neurological impairment in the ASP organic subjects was not nearly so severe as was that of Strauss' subjects.

In the present study a special effort was made to assure understanding and motivation on the part of the subject, toward the task he was to perform. Many of the studies referred to previously have contained groups selected for the most characteristic representatives for the two categories. Our sampling procedure was different; the subjects were originally selected on the basis of age and IQ, and the etiological classification was done only subsequently. This means that all shades of organics and familials are included in the present population, indicating that differences, which may occur in extreme groups, disappear when the groups are more inclusive. For this reason 19 extremely high and 19 extremely low scorers have been selected and their distribution over etiological categories recorded. Each group of 19 subjects was made up of five subjects from the youngest sample and seven subjects from each of the two older samples. No attempt was made to control for sex. Comparisons were made for each of the fifty variables plus *Mean* and *SD* of *T* score. This analysis showed that for the great majority of variables each etiological category was represented among the highest scorers, as well as among the lowest scorers. There were no clear differences—although there was a slight tendency for the Organics, the Mixed, and the Mongoloids to be found more often in the lowest than in the highest group; and for the Familials and the Unexplained to be more often among the highest than the lowest scorers. An attempt to identify discriminating variables was unsuccessful, since no variable sufficed to segregate the high or low scorers within the etiologies. Of considerable interest is the finding that among extremes of IQ were encountered all etiological groups except the mongoloid, which contained only extremely low scorers. Since these findings so clearly contradict the existing notion of poorer performance by organic subjects, it seems reasonable to assume that the heavier representation of an etiological category in the lowest or highest group for any of the variables was a chance occurrence. It must be concluded that there is no relationship between performance level on specific tasks or across tasks, and etiological classification. Thus it appears that the psychological tests of the present study are of limited value in making a differential diagnosis.

One would tend to agree with Werner and Thuma's (1942 a) conclusion that the mechanisms of integration are impaired in the brain injured children. It is, however, reasonable to consider that impaired integration is characteristic of all retarded children, whether they are brain damaged or not. The question is: What actually is meant by saying that integration is impaired? It seems safe to predict that disagreement will continue for some time on this question. On the other hand, advances in neurophysiology may give further insight into these mechanisms.

CORRELATION BETWEEN MEASURES

Theories of normal mental development have emphasized that psychological functioning and cerebral organization show an increase in differentiation and integration with increased age up to maturity (Hebb, 1949; Lewin, 1935; Werner, 1942). Hebb has presented a theory of the neurophysiological basis for these developmental processes. It has furthermore been assumed that this normal developmental trend is interfered with in mental retardation (Benoit, 1957, 1959) and that differentiation and integration of psychological functions remain incomplete. One of the hypotheses on which the Ability Structure Project was based stated that for mental retardates—particularly individuals showing constitutional defects and generalized physiological involvement—differentiation of skills will occur to a lesser degree than for normals. It was anticipated that this tendency would be apparent in the heterogeneous samples of retardates in our population.

Differentiation is understood to be a process by which psychological functions change progressively from relative homogeneity to relative heterogeneity so that their various aspects are more independently utilized. Integration is used in the sense of an organizational process by which differentiated functions come to work together harmoniously. Since harmonious action among functions facilitates achievement, level of performance may be used as an index of integration. Although the interaction between the two is difficult to determine, it appears that differentiation is a prerequisite of integration.

It seems reasonable to assume that correlation coefficients between measures will reflect degree of differentiation. Since impaired differentiation has been predicted for the retardates, higher intercorrelation can be expected in the retardates than in the normals.

Higher correlations may come about in two ways: less differentiation among functions, making for some interdependence; or greater variability of the performance scores. Since the latter was found in the retarded samples where the IQ range was almost half the range of the normals, it seemed reasonable to assume that the greater variance itself was characteristic of the population. This fact—that it was the restricted sample which had the greater variance—seemed to be a strong argument that the higher correlations might be interpreted in terms of differentiation to which the variance itself was initially tied. This argument was supported by the finding that correlations were in the predicted direction and that certain functions which should reasonably be considered differentiated by age 8-10 (e.g., sensory functions) did in fact show as low correlation for the retardates as for the normals.

On these grounds it might be expected that level of performance (integration) is inversely related to the magnitude of the correlations between variables (differentiation). To assess this question, correlations were obtained between the Mean *T* score for the sample, and the mean correlation between each variable and all the other variables. The correlations were −.63, −.25, and −.30 for the three samples respectively, which is significant at the 5% level. The decrease in relation for the older samples seemed to be primarily due to decrease in variability of performance level (integration), while overall differentiation remained relatively constant (mean total correlations .20, .19, and .21 respectively).

Correlation matrices for the four samples appear in the Appendices. Inspection of these tables reveals that the majority of the correlation coefficients in all four samples were quite low. Moderate or high correlations were found when the same measure was obtained for both sides (or different planes) of the body, such as Audiometry L and R (r range for the four samples .50 – .75), Kinesthesis L and R (.39 – .61), Two-Point Threshold L and R (.66 – .80), Ataxiometer M and L (.34 – .59), Grip L and R (.89 – .92), and Pegboard L and R (.66 – .89). It was interesting to note the trend toward higher correlation for the retardates in these measures. Only once did the normal sample have the highest correlation, while three times it had the lowest correlation. The means of these six correlations for Samples 1 to

4 were .74, .72, .66, and .61 respectively. Variance was similar between retarded samples, hence the systematic decrease in correlation coefficient from Sample 1 to 3 may be regarded as reflecting a continuous process of differentiation.

The low correlations seen in the Appendices indicate that the functions measured by the Ability Structure test battery are highly specific functions. Contrary to the expectation that the present study would make it possible to select a reduced battery with a maximum of discriminatory power; the four correlation matrices showed that if a truly comprehensive mapping of functions was to be obtained, a larger test battery might be necessary. The task of identifying ability patterns among retarded individuals is therefore a considerably more complex task than was originally expected.

Correlation coefficients will reflect differentiation only when variables reflect independent processes. On this basis, duplicate measures of the same tasks have been eliminated in the subsequent analysis. In general, this amounts to discarding measures obtained on one side of the body. For example, in Pegboard only Pegboard L was retained, while Pegboard R and B were discarded. Similarly, Simple Visual RT was discarded while Simple Auditory RT was retained, since both were considered to be measuring the same essential task. On the basis of its high correlation with the other complex tasks, PMA was eliminated. The measures, Choice RT and Scrambled Foreperiod RT, as well as Azimuth Arithmetic and Reversals, were considered to have extensive overlapping. Since they were found to have high correlations in retardates—though not in normals—they were retained. This difference seems best explained by differentiation interpretation. The complete list of variables retained may be seen in Table 23.

Inspection of the reduced matrices indicated that there was a general trend toward lower correlations in the normal sample than in the three retarded samples. For the purpose of an overall comparison, the mean of the correlation coefficients—regardless of signs—was computed. The mean correlations were .16, .18, .19 and .13 in the four samples respectively.

If it can be assumed that the three retarded samples were similarly constituted, the means of the correlation coefficients indicate that differentiation in the older retarded samples had progressed no more than in the youngest sample. Even 20-24 year old retardates had not reached the degree of differentiation found in the 8-10 year old normals. The implication of this was that the process of differentiation in a retarded population is completed at the age of 8-10 years. This is, however, a tenuous conclusion, since the possibility of selection factors needs to be considered. It seems reasonable to assume that retardates who remain institutionalized beyond the age of 20 are the more incapacitated individuals. There is also reason to believe that the youngest retardates represented a selection due to a greater exclusion from this sample of those individuals who were not able to perform the tasks. These considerations are given some support by the Mean IQ of the retarded samples: 57, 52, and 49 respectively, and by the general performance level of the 20-24 sample. It thus appears that the gradual increase in overall mean correlations across the retarded samples may have been a result of selection factors.

A further break-down of the means of the correlation coefficients is presented in Table 20 where mean intercorrelation across variables—grouped according to domains of functions—has been computed. These correlations showed considerable variation between the different domains. The differences in the correlation coefficients across the four samples were often small, but the trends were consistent, and each correlation mean was based on a rather high number of correlations. The normal subjects, Sample 4, had the lowest correlation in all but one combination (sensory-sensory). The correlations in the oldest retarded sample were generally higher than in the 12-15 sample. The relationship between the youngest and the 12-15 sample was inconsistent: the youngest sample had lower correlations for motor and perceptual combinations, and higher correlations for sensory and complex combinations.

Within domains of measures the sensory and perceptual variables had the lowest correlations, followed by the motor measures and the complex measures. Relationships between sensory and motor tasks and between sensory and perceptual tasks seemed to be rather weak and only slightly stronger between motor and perceptual tasks. The relationship between complex functions and the other categories of measures seemed to form a hierarchy, with sensory tasks lowest; perceptual tasks next; and motor tasks showing the strongest relationship. Since many of the perceptual tasks required discrimination and judgement, one might have expected higher correlations for the perceptual-complex than for the motor-complex combinations. This was indeed the case for the normal subjects; and the rather strong relationship between motor and complex measures seemed to be a characteristic of the retardates.

Since there appeared to be rather distinct levels of correlation in these combinations across samples, it may be of interest to examine the inter-correlations within the various categories of variables. The sensory-sensory correlations were all low and may be interpreted as

TABLE 20

MEAN CORRELATIONS (WITH DECIMAL POINT OMITTED) AND NUMBER AND PERCENTAGE OF CORRELATION COEFFICIENTS ABOVE .39, GROUPED ACCORDING TO TYPE OF MEASUREMENT FOR THE FOUR SAMPLES

		SENSORY				*MOTOR*				*PERCEPT*				*COMPLEX*			
		1	*2*	*3*	*4*	*1*	*2*	*3*	*4*	*1*	*2*	*3*	*4*	*1*	*2*	*3*	*4*
	Mean	16	13	15	14	14	13	14	11	14	11	11	11	21	15	17	12
Sensory	N	6	6	6	3	7	7	8	0	8	2	1	2	5	3	2	0
	%	9.1	9.1	9.1	4.5	3.1	3.1	3.5	0.0	4.8	1.2	.6	1.2	8.3	5.0	3.3	0.0
	Mean					31	32	34	21	17	19	21	13	32	34	35	15
Motor	N					56	48	68	16	13	27	31	3	28	41	47	3
	%					32.8	28.1	39.8	9.4	4.9	10.2	11.7	1.1	29.5	43.2	49.5	3.2
	Mean									14	15	16	13	24	26	26	20
Percept	N									5	4	5	0	16	24	18	6
	%									5.5	4.4	5.5	0.0	22.9	34.3	25.7	8.6
	Mean													63	56	59	47
Complex	N													10	9	9	5
	%													100.0	90.0	90.0	50.0

meaning that a high degree of differentiation is reached by the age of 8-10, with relatively little difference between normals and retardates. The perceptual-perceptual correlations showed much the same level and the same pattern. By comparison, motor measures did not seem to have reached the same degree of differentiation and the difference between the retardates and the normals was more pronounced. The complex measures had the highest correlations; i.e., they showed the least amount of differentiation.

If hypothetical curves are fitted to these correlations (Fig. 6), it appears that the youngest retarded sample had lower correlations (higher degree of differentiation) and the oldest sample higher correlations (less differentiation) than these curves would indicate. This may be a result of the positive selection of the youngest and the negative selection of the oldest sample discussed above.

The curves in Fig. 6, with allowance for the selection factor, indicate that in the retardates the process of differentiation levels off earlier for sensory and perceptual functions than for motor functions, with complex functions last. The figure indicates furthermore that subject selection operates differentially according to level of differentiation reached.

It appears from this analysis that motor tasks, which have less differentiation than have perceptual tasks (implying either more difficult differentiations or more elements to differentiate), may be considered far more complex than the perceptual tasks. The similarity of the correlations for sensory and perceptual tasks may reflect the difficulties in distinguishing such functions.

These results are regarded as a confirmation of the hypothesis that retarded subjects show less differentiation of skills than do normal subjects. The differences are most pronounced for motor and complex mental functions, less for perceptual functions and least for sensory functions. One implication of this is that complex (intellectual) measures are more indicative of general level of performance in retardates than in normals.

Since the complete as well as the reduced correlation matrices were so big and since they contained so many low correlations, they were difficult to comprehend. To make the information of the reduced matrices more accessible, a composite table (Table 21) has been constructed. The entries have been limited to those variables for which at least one sample attained a correlation above .39. The selection of .39 as a critical value (about the .1% level of confidence for the *N*s in question) was arbitrary but considered to be a reasonable distinction between low and moderately high correlation coefficients.

TABLE 21

CORRELATION COEFFICIENTS FROM THE REDUCED MATRICES FOR COMBINATIONS WHERE AT LEAST ONE SAMPLE EXCEEDED CRITERION LEVEL

		Vis. Acuity	Color Vis.	Audio. L	Speech Thres.	Kinesth. L	Grip L	Lower Arm	Tapping	Audio. RT	Audio. Choice RT	Scrambled RT	Hand Prec. Hits	Pegboard L	Railwalking	Word Assoc.	Percep. Speed	Span of Appreh.	Ident. Thresh.	Recogn.	Azimuth, Arith.	Azimuth, Rev.	Brightn. Discr.	CFF	Stereogn.	Weight Lift.	Porteus I.Q.	Raven
Vis. Acuity	1		54					36		23				42	44			53	41	29								
	2		52					42		10				40	44			47	29	42								
	3		56					43		40				42	45			28	38	49								
	4		23					19		−05				23	12			25	42	30								
Color Vis.*	1																		44									
	2																		24									
	3																		31									
	4																		15									
Audio. L*	1																25						45					
	2																13						01					
	3																14						−04					
	4																43						13					
Speech Thres.*	1							−02																				
	2							44																				
	3							08																				
	4							02																				
Kinesth. L*	1																	48			44							45
	2																	14			06							18
	3																	16			24							25
	4																	−02			06							−06
Grip L	1								41	47	42	47	46	59	25						42				39		44	
	2								21	28	40	30	21	38	52						37				32		35	
	3								19	21	27	25	30	50	36						18				44		34	
	4								17	21	01	35	−03	46	23						15				23		01	
Lower Arm	1								45	42	33	34	22	31	24			33		19	22	41			23	−01	37	33
	2								60	45	47	57	25	58	51			44		28	41	39			58	16	42	37
	3								62	60	43	41	44	44	39			31		44	27	22			41	42	43	43
	4								30	35	09	29	11	31	07			07		20	38	13			−01	03	03	21
Tapping	1									40	48	51	32	45	26			48		18					24		34	
	2									34	32	31	12	46	34			37		46					48		43	
	3									53	49	51	47	54	42			33		44					46		41	
	4									22	13	30	−07	44	42			22		14					14		14	
Audio. RT	1										51	64		46												16	41	34
	2										67	75		39												16	34	14
	3										50	63		42												40	45	45
	4										23	35		14												−01	13	20
Audio. Choice RT	1											62		28	24	07										10	47	
	2											66		38	40	41										09	29	
	3											56		50	46	26										44	36	
	4											23		−10	13	09										29	08	
Scram-	1												27	46	33		19	45		28					20	19	40	32
	2												19	32	41		31	23		15					38	13	33	12

bled RT	3	43	59	46	40	38	41				43	41	51	40
	4	−21	26	20	23	23	24				−03	−09	16	12
Hand Prec. Hits	1		32	18					42		39			
	2		42	38					32		38			
	3		55	53					18		40			
	4		−13	−01					−06		03			
Peg-board L	1			55		49	28	36	35		45	07	48	43
	2			56		46	47	47	41		55	12	47	44
	3			68		43	45	39	31		55	47	47	46
	4			34		37	20	30	18		30	−22	21	20
Rail-walking	1					41		19			39		31	
	2					38		43			44		44	
	3					35		27			46		44	
	4					22		−02			−02		02	
Word Assoc.	1				19									
	2				31									
	3				52									
	4				05									
Percep. Speed	1									21				
	2									43				
	3									24				
	4									−03				
Span of Appreh.	1						55	53	43		46		53	50
	2						49	32	18		49		43	49
	3						37	26	33		32		34	38
	4						25	29	23		26		20	33
Ident. Thresh.	1													
	2													
	3													
	4													
Recogn.	1										39		26	39
	2										39		49	44
	3										43		47	51
	4										29		27	33
Azimuth, Arith.	1								57		37		56	64
	2								66		38		51	53
	3								62		46		46	56
	4								32		23		25	36
Azimuth, Rev.	1										25		55	48
	2										32		42	41
	3										54		39	43
	4										13		29	38
Brightn. Discr.	1													
	2													
	3													
	4													
CFF	1													
	2													
	3													
	4													
Stereogn.	1												43	38
	2												46	40
	3												52	56
	4												23	35
Weight Lift.	1													
	2													
	3													
	4													
Porteus I.Q.	1													54
	2													49
	3													67
	4													38

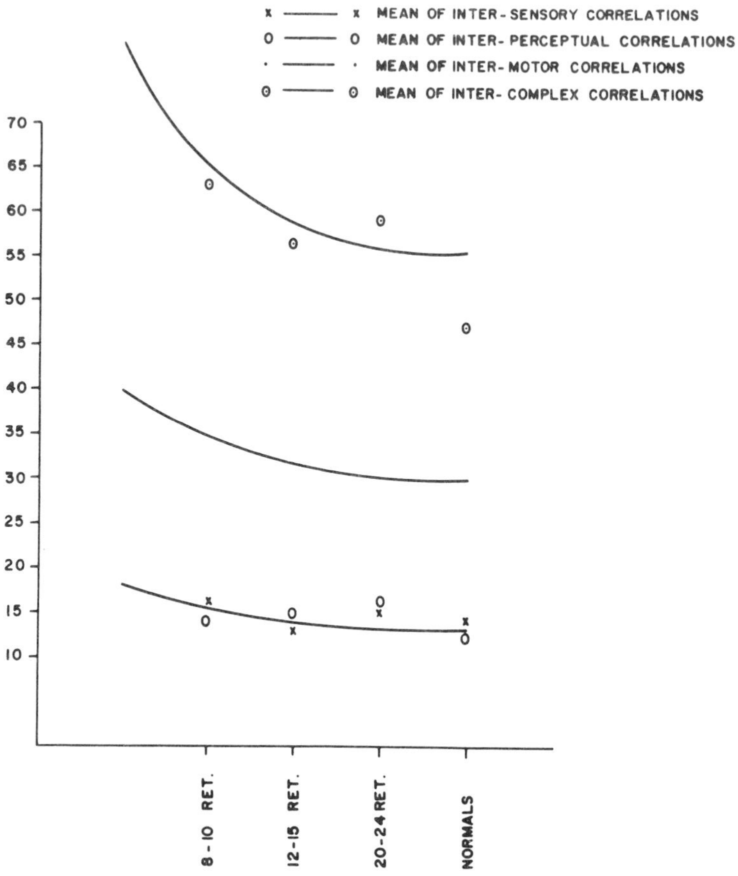

Figure 6. Hypothetical curves of differentiation, from mean correlations within various domains of measures.

Nine variables did not exceed the critical value of .39 when correlated with any other variable for either of the four samples: Hand Dominance, Eye Dominance, Kinesthesis R, Two-Point Threshold L, Ataxiometry M, Mirror Drawing Total Time, Time Interval Estimation, Muller-Lyer Extent, and Muller-Lyer Anticipation. These are highly specific, independent measures representing the maximum of differentiation; this differentiation was little impaired in the retardates. It is interesting to note that psychomotor measures (excepting Mirror Drawing Total Time which is more heavily influenced by the integration of visual cues) and measures of complex mental function are lacking from the list. Several of these tests are among the seven previously considered for exclusion from the battery on the grounds that they did not discriminate between normals and retardates: Hand Dominance, Eye Dominance, Time Interval Estimation, and the two Muller-Lyer measures.

Some additional measures also showed little intercorrelation in any of the four samples: Brightness Discrimination and CFF had only a single criterion correlation; Word Association, Speech Threshold, and Audiometry had only two; Color Vision, Kinesthesis, and I.D. Threshold had three, while RT to Pictures and Weight Lifting had five. Thus, of the 33 tests in the battery, 18 (20 measures) might be considered as relatively independent.

Only one correlation coefficient exceeded the critical value of .39 in all four samples; namely, Pegboard to Tapping.

In 19 instances, all three retarded samples had correlations above .39 while the normals had correlations below that level. These correlations indicated the functions where differentiation was specifically impaired in the retarded. Their distribution over categories of measures is entered in Table 22. These correlations tended to cluster in the motor-motor (6) and perceptual-complex (4) categories. This was another expression of the trend seen in Table 17, the tendency of retardates to have high correlations between motor measures.

The correlations discussed so far represent the combinations where there was a high degree of agreement between samples. For the majority of the correlations, however, there was little agreement between samples, and no patterns seemed to be present.

Another way of appraising the intercorrelations between measures was to count how often each single variable reached a correlation coefficient above .39 in its combination with the other 34 measures of the reduced matrix. Such counts for each sample are shown in Table 23. The table reviews and further specifies points already made. The retarded samples had many more correlations above .39 than had the normal sample. Among the retardates there was an increasing number of such correlations with increasing age, and while the selective sampling may have contributed to this result, it supports the notion that little differentiation takes place after the age of 8-10 in the retardates.

The normals had few criterion correlations for the same variables where the retardates had high incidence rate. This is compatible with the view that the more frequent criterion correlations in the retarded indicate less differentiation; i.e., an arrested development process, in comparison with the normals. The data suggest that it is a quantita-

TABLE 22

THE COMBINATION OF MEASURES WHERE FOR THE REDUCED MATRIX ALL THREE RETARDED SAMPLES HAVE CORRELATIONS ABOVE .39, ARRANGED ACCORDING TO DOMAINS OF MEASURES

	SENSORY	*MOTOR*	*PERCEPTUAL*	*COMPLEX*
SENSORY	Vis. Acuity-Color Vis.	Pegb.-Vis. Acuity Railw.-Vis. Acuity		
MOTOR		Tapping-Lower Arm Aud. Ch. RT-Aud. RT Scramb. RT-Aud. Ch. RT Railw.-Pegb. Aud. RT-Lower Arm Scramb. RT-Aud. RT	Span. Appreh.-Pegb. Stereogn.-Pegb.	Porteus IQ-Pegb. Raven-Pegb.
PERCEPTUAL			Azim. Rev.-Azim. Arith.	Porteus IQ-Azim. Arith. Porteus IQ-Stereogn. Raven-Azim. Rev. Raven-Azim. Arith.
COMPLEX				Raven-Porteus IQ

TABLE 23

Number of Times Each Measure of the Reduced Matrices Correlates at Criterion Level with Each of the Other Measures. (Asterisks Indicate Specific Functions)

Test	*8–10*	*12–15*	*20–24*	*Normals*
Hand Dom.*	0	0	0	0
Eye Dom.*	0	0	0	0
Vis. Acuity	6	6	5	1
Color Vis.*	2	0	1	0
Audio. L.*	1	1	0	0
Speech Thres.*	0	2	0	0
Kinesth. L.*	3	0	0	0
2-Point L.*	0	0	0	0
Atax. M.*	0	0	0	0
Grip L	8	2	2	1
Lower Arm	3	12	12	0
Tapping	7	5	10	2
Aud. RT	7	3	9	0
Aud. Choice RT	5	6	7	0
Scrambled RT	7	4	12	0
Hand Pres. Hits	2	1	6	0
Pegboard L	10	12	15	2
Mirr. Dr. T. T.*	0	0	0	0
Railwalking	3	9	8	1
Word Assoc.*	0	1	1	0
Percep. Speed*	0	1	3	1
Span of Appreh.	12	7	1	0
Ident. Thresh.*	2	0	0	1
Recogn.	1	6	7	0
Azimuth Arith.	6	6	4	0
Azimuth Rev.	5	4	3	0
Brightn. Discr.*	1	0	0	0
CFF*	0	1	0	0
Stereogn.	3	7	12	0
Time Int. Est.*	0	0	0	0
Weight Lift.*	0	0	5	0
Muller-L. Ext.*	0	0	0	0
Muller-L. Antic.*	0	0	0	0
Porteus I Q	11	10	9	0
Raven	6	7	9	0
TOTAL	111	113	141	9

tive rather than a qualitative difference, and would lead one to wonder if normal children younger than 8-10 would have as high correlations as the retardates.

The information from Table 23 allows a subdivision of the measures into two categories, consisting of those which reflect specific, independent functions, showing few criterion correlations (marked with an asterisk), and those measures which are not independent. The latter common functions are defined as variables which have at least nine criterion correlations. In general, the specific functions tend to be sensory or perceptual, while the common functions tend to be motor and complex.

Further comments on the correlations presented in Table 21 will be limited to a general review of the relationships which existed between variables reflecting common functions, in order to determine which functions are least differentiated in the retardates.

Visual Acuity reached the criterion correlation in the normals only for ID Threshold. For the retardates, however, Visual Acuity was related to Color Vision, Pegboard, and Railwalking and more inconsistently to Lower Arm Movement, Apprehension Span, and Recognition. One may thus conclude that Visual Acuity is a markedly more independent measure in the normals than in the retardates. This finding is consistent with impaired attention and alertness in the retardates.

Grip L reached criterion correlation primarily for the youngest retarded sample. These correlations were with Tapping, Auditory RT, Auditory Choice RT, Scrambled Foreperiod, Hand Precision Hits, Purdue, Stereognosis, Azimuth Arithmetic, and Porteus IQ. The 12-15 sample had criterion correlation for Auditory Choice RT and Railwalking, while the oldest sample had such correlation for Pegboard and Stereognosis. The normal sample had criterion correlation only for Pegboard. From the relations of the youngest sample it seemed that a certain minimum muscular strength was necessary to perform adequately on tasks which involved the musculature of the hand in manipulation and coordination, indicating lack of differentiation for these functions. It was interesting to note that Lower Arm Movement, involving the more general musculature of the arm, was not related, even though Railwalking was, for one sample. While Grip was differentiated from manipulation and coordination of the hand in the two oldest samples, the differentiation between strength and finger dexterity remained impaired. If one remembers that the two older samples surpassed the normal sample in Strength of Grip but not in Purdue Pegboard, it can be seen that the importance of finger coordination, rather than strength per se, was emphasized by these relationships. In the young retardates the lack of coordination, in addition to intellectual limitation, may also have contributed to a low Porteus score.

Lower Arm Movement was related to Speed of Tapping and to Auditory RT for all three retarded samples. Lower Arm had a relationship with the two remaining RTs and Purdue Pegboard for the two oldest retarded samples, as well as with Hand Precision Hits for the oldest, and with Railwalking for the 12-15 sample. Differentiation of Lower Arm Movement from other speed measures seemed to be impaired in all retarded samples. For the two older samples, differentiation of large muscle coordination from fine and gross coordination was also impaired.

Among the perceptual measures, Lower Arm Movement was related to Azimuth Reversals in the youngest retarded sample, to Apprehension Span and Azimuth Arithmetic in the 12-15 sample, to Recognition, (and inversely to Weight Lifting in the oldest), and to Stereognosis in the two oldest retarded samples. These last two perceptual measures may be accounted for in terms of hand coordination. Thus, the functions of Lower Arm Movement (motor speed and large muscle coordination) seemed to be less differentiated from appraisal of spatial relations in the two younger samples, from Span of Apprehension in the 12-15, from tactual-visual integration in the two older samples, and from recognition in the oldest. It was apparent that differentiation of motor and perceptual components was more impaired in the retardates, especially in the oldest.

With but one exception (Raven for the 12-15 sample), Lower Arm Movement was related to both intelligence measures in the two oldest samples, but not in the normal and youngest retarded samples. That differentiation of these two functions was less in the oldest samples was again probably a result of sampling factors.

Speed of Tapping has been mentioned above as related to Grip L and Lower Arm Movement. In addition, it was related to the three RTs for the youngest and oldest retardates and to Hand Precision Hits for the oldest retardates. All four samples showed relationship to Purdue Pegboards, and the normals and oldest retardates showed relationship to Railwalking. Among the perceptual measures the youngest sample showed relationship to Span of Apprehension, while the two older retarded samples showed relationship to Recognition of Non-meaningful Material and Stereognosis. Only the two oldest retarded samples showed a relationship to the intellectual measures.

The motor speed and the coordination component of the tapping task were thus not differentiated from fine finger coordination and possibly not from gross bodily coordination. The perceptual measures included were those also less differentiated from Lower Arm. As was the case for Lower Arm Movement, the selection factor may have been responsible for the higher correlations with intellectual measures in the two older samples.

All three *RT Measures* have shown relationships, in one or more of the subject samples, to motor measures already considered. Intercorrelations between the three RT measures were relatively high for all three retarded samples, but were all relatively low (below .35) for the normals. In addition, RT measures were related to a number of other motor measures—most consistently to Pegboard L and Railwalking in the retarded samples. The normals had no criterion correlation between RT and any other motor tasks.

It appeared that differentiation of the various motor speed components of RT, e.g., response initiation from fine—and possibly from gross—motor coordination was impaired in the retardates. The same tendency was seen from the correlation between Lower Arm and Tapping. The trend was less evident in the 12-15 sample than in the other two retarded samples. In this connection, it may be remembered that the 12-15 sample reached a higher level of performance than did the other two in motor tasks.

Relationship between RT and perceptual measures, with two exceptions (Scrambled Foreperiod to Span of Apprehension, for the youngest retardates, and Auditory Choice to Word Association, for the 12-15 retardates), was limited to the oldest retarded sample. Here Scrambled RT was related to Speed of Perception (RT to Pictures), Recognition of Non-meaningful Material, Stereognosis, and inversely to Weight Lifting. As was the case earlier, recognition and tactual visual integration showed impaired differentiation from motor speed components in the oldest retarded sample.

With regard to relationship between RT measures and complex measures, the youngest and oldest retarded samples showed a relationship to Porteus, while only the oldest showed relationship to Raven. No relationship was found to either of these complex measures for the 12-15 and normal samples. In line with the findings above, it appeared that the motor component of the Porteus was less differentiated in the retardates, especially in the youngest and oldest, while it seemed to be the perceptual components of Raven which were less differentiated by the oldest retardates.

It has been shown above that *Hand Precision* Hits was primarily correlated to motor measures in the oldest sample. The same relationship held also for Pegboard, Railwalking, and Stereognosis. The youngest sample reached criterion for Azimuth Reversals in addition to Grip, and the 12-15 sample reached criterion for Pegboard L only. Whereas Strength of Grip seemed to be poorly differentiated by the youngest retardates from the hand manipulation required by Hand Precision Hits, the oldest retardates seemed to have attained this differentiation, but hand manipulation seemed to be less differentiated from other motor components in the oldest retardates. The most consistent trend in the retardates was that the integration of visual-tactual cues of Stereognosis seemed to be less differentiated from hand manipulation, even though only the oldest sample reached criterion.

The *Purdue Pegboard* has been involved in all the correlations considered above. For the remaining motor measure, Railwalking, relationship to Purdue Pegboard was found for all three retarded samples. Thus fine muscle, or finger, coordination seemed to be less differentiated from large muscle and gross bodily coordination in the retardates. With regard to perceptual measures, Purdue was related to Span of Apprehension and Stereognosis for the three retarded samples. It was related to Recognition of Non-meaningful Material for the two oldest samples, while the 12-15 year old sample showed relationship to Azimuth Arithmetic and Reversals. The oldest sample also showed an inverse relationship to Weight Lifting. Again, impaired differentiation was indicated between fine muscle coordination and the perceptual components of apprehension span, tactual visual integration, recognition, and appraisal of spatial relations.

All three retarded samples showed relationship to the two complex measures, indicating that the intellectual components were poorly differentiated from fine muscle coordination.

In addition to the sporadic relationship of *Railwalking* to Visual Acuity, Grip, Lower Arm Movement, Tapping, Auditory Choice RT, Scrambled Foreperiod RT, Hand Precision Hits, and the more systematic relationship to Purdue Pegboard; Railwalking was also related to Span of Apprehension for the youngest group, to Azimuth Arithmetic for the 12-15, to Stereognosis and Porteus IQ for the two older retarded samples. While the trends were not very strong or consistent, it may be observed that the quick appraisal of spatial relations, characteristic for Apprehension Span and Azimuth, and the integration of these relations with tactual kinesthetic cues (Stereognosis and Porteus), may be the functions which have impaired differentiation from the gross motor components of Railwalking in the retardates.

The perceptual measures of *Span of Apprehension, Recognition of Non-meaningful Material, Azimuth,* and *Stereognosis* have been related to a number of motor measures above. These four measures were also interrelated in varying degrees. Span of Apprehension was related to Recognition and to Stereognosis for the two younger retarded samples; to Azimuth Arithmetic and Reversals for the youngest sample. Recognition and Azimuth Arithmetic were related to Stereognosis for the oldest sample, while Azimuth Arithmetic was related to Azimuth Reversals for all three retarded samples. In contrast to the normals, who did not have criterion correlations for any of these measures, it was apparent that the retardates had impaired differentiation for perceptual functions involved in these four tasks. These functions appeared to be apprehension span, recognition, appraisal of spatial relations, and integration of visual-tactual cues. The four perceptual measures were also widely related to the two complex measures in the retardates, which indicated impaired differentiation from intellectual functions.

Finally the relationships between *complex measures* and motor and perceptual measures may be reviewed as follows:

The motor-complex relationships were more general for Porteus in all retarded samples, while Raven relationships were found primarily in the oldest sample. Purdue Pegboard seemed to be the one motor measure which had high correlations to both complex measures for all three retarded samples.

Both complex tasks were widely related to the perceptual tasks of Apprehension Span, Recognition, Azimuth, and Stereognosis in the retardates. Raven was seen to be more highly related to these perceptual tasks than it was to motor tasks. The normals had no criterion correlations between complex measures and any of the perceptual measures.

There are few studies in the literature which report correlation between ASP measures for a retarded population. Where sensory, motor, and perceptual measures are concerned, the reports are so few and scattered that there is little purpose in reviewing them. The situation is not as destitute when it comes to the relations between intelligence measures and a variety of other variables.

There are, as a matter of fact, many more reports in the literature on the relationship between the type of tasks included in the ASP battery and MA than can be reviewed here. The present survey has been limited to comments on this relationship in publications which for other reasons have been considered for the present study.

Porteus (1959) has reviewed studies for the Maze tests in comparison with other variables, spanning the period from 1922 to 1936. For the most part, these correlations concerned intelligence scales, performance scales or their subtests. A correlation of .48 was reported between the Maze test and Tapping for 110 school children.

In a group of 104 high grade institutionalized males, Tizard (1950) found a mean Porteus Maze IQ of 82.6, considerably higher than the present IQ score of 56 for the oldest retarded sample, which most closely approximated the age of Tizard's group. He found a correlation of .52 between Porteus and Raven, which was decidedly lower than the correlation of .67 found by us. This difference is in accordance with our conclusion about a relationship between performance level and differentiation.

A tentative conclusion was reached by Metheny (1941) that in normals the correlation between mental ability and strength of grip is very slightly positive or zero. Distefano et al. (1958) found correlations of .03 and .26, for males and females respectively, between Hand Dynamometer and MA. For Grip R the present study found higher correlations in retardates than in normals to all three intelligence tests. A slight positive correlation in the normals is in accordance with Metheny.

Simple and Choice RT were correlated to MA for organic and familial retarded subjects by Bensberg and Cantor (1957). Correlations in the former group were not significant, and in the latter group −.57 for simple and −.64 for the disjunctive task. A correlation of −.54 between MA and RT was reported by Ellis and Sloan (1957 a). The relationship was found to be rectilinear and almost entirely independent of the small, but statistically significant regression of RT upon CA. For 27 male mental defectives Pascal et al. (1951) found a correlation (rho) of −.61 between delayed reaction and Stanford-Binet MA. In the present study the data have been so organized that good performance always gave high scores, with the result that the correlation coefficients here were positive. For the three retarded samples the four RT were correlated to PMA-MA in the .32-.51 range, while they were considerably lower, .06-.31, for the normals. Except for 12-15 year olds with the Raven (where the correlation was comparable to the normals), the correlations of the four reaction times to the three intelligence measures ranged from .24-.51 in the retardates. Thus our results seem to correspond with those mentioned above.

Ellis and Sloan (1957 b) found a correlation coefficient of .43, with CA partialled out, between Stanford-Binet MA and rotary pursuit in mental retardates. ASP's Hand Precision task had certain features in common with a rotary pursuit task. The correlations to all three intelligence tests ranged from .17 to .42 for Hits and from .21 to .48 for Errors in the retardates. In normals the corresponding ranges were from −.01 to .10 for Hits and from −.07 to .30 for Errors. Thus the correlations were considerably higher for retardates than for normals, except for Error in the youngest retarded sample.

Two studies have reported correlation between MA and Purdue Pegboard for retarded populations. For 166 retardates over 12 years of age, Eyman et al. (1959) found a correlation coefficient of .47 to RLB. Tobias and Gorelick (1960) reported the following result for 73 non-institutionalized retarded adults in relating RLB to WAIS scores: .56 to Full Scale, .57 to performance items and .34 to verbal items. Our results for retardates were in a similar range (.32 to .57) but for the normals somewhat lower (.20 to .51).

Ellis et al. (1957) correlated their Mirror Drawing results to MA and found −.27 for Total Errors and non-significant correlation for Total Time. In the present study, Total Errors correlated from .23 to .51 for the retardates and .25 to .37 for the normals, while Total Time correlated from −.13 to .31 for the retardates and −.11 to −.21 for the normals. These results are more in agreement with the lower correlation for Total Time rather than for Total Errors, in spite of the fact that Ellis used a paper and pencil version of the test which resulted in considerably longer Total Times (see comments on Mirror Drawing).

Correlations for Railwalking and MA have been reported by Heath (1942) and Distefano et al. (1958). Heath found a correlation of .66 in a group of familial defectives but close to zero correlations for a "non-familial" group. Distefano found .04 for institutionalized males (Mean MA 9.9 and Mean CA 19.7) and .32 for females (Mean MA 9.1 and Mean CA 22.3). It is difficult to make any comparisons with our correlations—which ranged from .26 to .48 in the retardates and from .01 to .23 in the normals—since in the present study correlations were not available for etiological subgroups or for sex groups separately.

It appears in general, that investigators have regarded it more promising to establish relationships between level of intelligence to motor functions than to perceptual functions. The consensus of opinion seems to be that there is a positive relationship between MA and motor proficiency. Some authors would add that the statement has to be qualified by consideration of etiological factors.

Attenborough and Farber (1934) found higher correlations between motor abilities and intelligence in retarded subjects than had been reported for normal subjects. This finding was confirmed by the present study.

The comparisons of the present data with those quoted from the literature suffered sometimes from lack of conformity with respect to age range, MA range, level, etc. On this background there appears to be a high degree of agreement between present and previous findings.

The opening statement in an article by Berkson (1960 a) reads as follows: "Although it is commonly believed that reaction time and general intelligence are unrelated, studies employing the mentally deficients as Ss consistently demonstrate a positive correlation between speed of reaction and intelligence." Our data indicate that the statement may be generalized to include other aspects of motor functioning.

SUMMARY

In summarizing the discussion of impairment of the differentiation process, it may first be noted that using a correlation coefficient of .39 as criterion, there was no evidence that sensory functions, with the possible exception of visual acuity, were less differentiated in retardates than in normals.

With the exception of strength of grip in the two oldest retarded samples, there seemed to be a general lack of differentiation of motor functions in the retardates. The different levels of muscular coordination (finger, hand, arm, and gross body coordination) showed impaired differentiation from each other and from strength of grip, motor speed, and response initiation.

There was also a general lack of differentiation between motor and perceptual domains in the retardates. Thus motor speed and apprehension span lacked in differentiation (especially in the younger samples) while in the oldest sample this lack was observed between gross body movement and quick appraisal of spatial relations, recognition, and integration of tactual-kinesthetic cues. Lack of differentiation was also suggested between hand manipulation and visual-tactual cues; again, particularly in the older samples.

Several of the perceptual functions did not seem to show less differentiation in the retardates: perceptual speed, appraisal of temporal durations, susceptibility to illusions, discrimination of brightness, and the temporal resolving power of the eye. Those which did show less differentiation seem to involve apprehension span, appraisal of spatial relations, recognition, and integration of tactual-visual information. The younger retarded sample showed this lack primarily for the first two functions, while the older retardates showed it more for the last two.

Intellectual functions showed impaired differentiation from fine motor coordination in all retarded samples. There was also lack of differentiation of strength, motor speed, large muscle, and gross motor coordination from intellectual functions. This was primarily found for the first two from Porteus in the youngest sample and for the last three from Raven, as well as Porteus, in the oldest samples.

Considering differentiation of intellectual from perceptual functions, ASP found that there was a lack of differentiation from appraisal of spatial relations in all three retarded samples; from apprehension span in the two youngest; and from recognition and integration of tactual-visual cues primarily in the two oldest samples.

Finally, with regard to complex functions, the evidence was limited to perceptual abstraction functions of Raven being poorly differentiated from perceptual motor components of Porteus in the retarded.

It may be noted as a general trend that motor functions were affected more by lack of differentiation than were perceptual functions. There was also a general tendency for the simpler tasks to be affected in the youngest (strength, apprehension span, and spatial relations) while the more complex tasks were affected in the oldest sample (motor coordination, recognition, and integration of tactual-visual cues).

MULTIVARIATE ANALYSIS

TRADITIONAL FACTOR ANALYSIS

Factor analysis provided a technique for assessing the existence of general and specific functions tapped by the test battery. There seems to be no factor analysis reported in the literature on sensory, motor, perceptual, and complex tasks for retarded subjects. It was therefore of theoretical interest to perform a factor analysis on the data, particularly with respect to whether or not the same factor structure is found in retarded as in normal subjects. The result of the factor analysis may also be an asset in the subsequent attempt of subdividing the population samples into groups with similar ability structures. The description of such groups may be greatly facilitated if it can be done in terms of factors rather than as specific test results. Finally there is the practical consideration that the administration of 34 tests is a very arduous task, especially with the youngest retardates. The reduction of the battery to more manageable proportions is a real problem to which factor analysis may contribute significantly.

The centroid method of factoring matrices was used for each of the four samples and the resulting factor matrices were rotated to simple structure by means of the quartimax matrix rotation procedure.[5] The centroid method of factoring was terminated after 15 factors had been extracted, and 12 of these were rotated to orthogonal simple structure.[6]

Theoretically, the quartimax rotation tends to maximize the difference between high and low loaded scales on a given factor, by making high loadings higher and low loadings lower. This tends to facilitate

[5] The factor analysis was done by the Service Bureau Corporation, New York, on an IBM 704, under the supervision of Mr. R. G. Johnson.

[6] The tables of factor loadings for each variable—separately for the four samples—may be obtained from American Documentation Institute.

interpretation. One may still have scales which are loaded significantly on more than one factor. Optimally a rotation should produce a pattern of loadings which is psychologically meaningful, but psychological meaningfulness is largely a matter of interpretation. The contribution to the total factor variance of the 15 factors is shown in Table 24. It is obvious that the 15 factors leave a considerable amount of unaccounted for variance. The table shows that the total variance for the 15 factors was inversely related to level of functioning of the four samples such as was expressed in the mean of the Mean *T* scores: the youngest retarded sample had the highest total variance and the lowest Mean *T* score (34.4), while the normal sample had the lowest total variance and the highest Mean *T* score (50.0). It seems that factor variance was related to general level and integration, more than to high intercorrelations and differentiation.

In interpreting the rotated factors the general directions suggested by Fruchter (1954) and Guilford (1961) have been employed; i.e., factor loadings of less than .30 have not been considered. The variables with loadings above .30 for each factor are presented in Tables 25, 26, 27 and 28. For each factor the variables have been arranged according to factor loading. In interpreting the factors the most reliable findings have been stressed, and the more general lines emphasized. Since four factor analyses were performed, special attention has been given to trends which occurred in two or more of the analyses. It has been assumed that high factor loadings may occur by chance and therefore unsupported loadings have largely been discarded.

TABLE 24

FACTOR VARIANCE FOR THE FOUR TRADITIONAL FACTOR ANALYSES

Factor	*8-10 Retarded*	*12-15 Retarded*	*20-24 Retarded*	*Normal*
I	.223	.231	.243	.155
II	.066	.057	.054	.051
III	.057	.047	.040	.054
IV	.052	.043	.044	.039
V	.043	.039	.034	.035
VI	.028	.031	.029	.031
VII	.031	.031	.030	.034
VIII	.028	.026	.031	.030
IX	.024	.026	.023	.026
X	.024	.023	.022	.024
XI	.024	.020	.022	.024
XII	.026	.019	.020	.018
XIII	.025	.017	.019	.017
XIV	.015	.016	.016	.018
XV	.017	.015	.016	.016
TOTAL	.681	.639	.642	.572

TABLE 25

FACTOR LOADINGS FOR THE 8–10 RETARDED SAMPLE

Factor I	*Factor II*	*Factor III*	*Factor IV*	*Factor V*	*Factor VI*
Pegboard B. 97	PMA-IQ −90	Audio. L. −79	Hand Prec. Hits. 70	2-Point L. 95	Atax. M. 68
Pegboard L. 89	PMA-MA −67	Audio. R. −75	Ident. Thresh. −43	2-Point R. 75	Atax. L. 66
Pegboard R. 88	Porteus IQ −64	Brightn. Discr. −48	2-Point R-L 34	2-Point R-L −35	Word Assoc. −38
Railwalking 65	Raven −63	Speech Thres. −44	Porteus MA 31	Mirr. Dr. Err. 35	Hand Prec. Err. 33
Grip L. 65	Azimuth Arith. −57		Azimuth Rev. 30	Porteus MA 32	
Grip R. 64	Porteus MA −51				
Vis RT. 60	Span of Appreh. −43				
Porteus MA 57	Kinesth. R. −37				
Span of Appreh. 54	Recogn. −37				
Stereogn. 52	Azimuth Rev. −36				
Tapping 51	CA 35				
Aud. RT. 51	Kinesth. L. −32				
Scrambled RT. 51	Aud. Choice RT. −32				
Hand Prec. Er. 49	Weight Lift. −30				
Vis. Acuity 46					
Porteus IQ 46					
PMA-MA 46					
CA 44					
Hand Prec. Hits 40					
Raven 38					
Azimuth Arith. 35					
Lower Arm 34					
Aud. Choice RT. 34					
Azimuth Rev. 34					

Factor VII	*Factor VIII*	*Factor IX*	*Factor X*	*Factor XI*	*Factor XII*
Mirr. Dr. Er. −74	Scrambled RT −60	Percep. Speed −58	Color Vis. 69	Hand Dom. −55	Kinesth. L. −52
Mirr. Dr. T.T. −62	Aud. RT. −59	Muller-L. Antic. 52	Vis. Acuity 58	Hand Prec. Er. −43	Kinesth. R. −48
Mirr. Dr. Er. R. −59	Aud. Choice RT. −53	Weight Lift. 45	Ident. Thres. 37	Speech Thres. 34	Brightn. Discr. 34
Kinesth. L. −38	Vis. RT. −41	Grip L. 39	2-Point R-L 36	Word Assoc. −34	Span of Appreh. −33
	Tapping 31	Ident. Thresh. −32	CFF 35	Tapping −33	Recogn. −30

TABLE 26

Factor Loadings for the 12–15 Retarded Sample

Factor I	*Factor II*	*Factor III*	*Factor IV*	*Factor V*	*Factor VI*
Pegboard L. 88	Aud. RT. 84	2-Point L. −79	Grip L. 76	Audio. L. −88	2-Point R-L −64
Pegboard B. 83	Vis. RT. 83	2-Point R. −73	Grip R. 74	Audio. R. −72	Muller-L. Antic. 36
Pegboard R. 82	Scrambled RT. 75	Mirr. Dr. Er. R. 44	CA 65	Speech Thres. −59	
Lower Arm 72	Aud. Choice RT. 67		Railwalking 33		
PMA-MA 70	Word Assoc. 33				
Stereogn. 69					
PMA-IQ 67					
Azimuth Arith. 63					
Tapping 62					
Porteus IQ 61					
Railwalking 61					
Porteus MA 60					
Recogn. 59					
Span of Appreh. 59					
Mirr. Dr. Er. 59					
Hand Prec. Err. 58					
Azimuth Rev. 56					
Raven 54					
Vis. Acuity 51					
Grip R. 51					
Grip L. 44					
Color Vis. 44					
Hand Prec. Hits 42					
Percep. Speed 41					
Speech Thres. 38					
Aud. Choice RT. 37					
Scrambled RT. 36					
CFF 35					
Aud. RT. 33					
Vis. RT. 33					
Atax. M. 30					

Factor VII	*Factor VIII*	*Factor IX*	*Factor X*	*Factor XI*	*Factor XII*
PMA-MA −51	Kinesth. R. −72	Porteus IQ −69	Percep. Speed 54	Color Vis. −41	Atax. L. 72
PMA-IQ −46	Kinesth. L. −67	Porteus MA −65	Azimuth Arith. −33	Vis. Acuity −38	Atax. M. 42
CFF 42	Muller-L. Antic. 32		Azimuth Rev. −33	Ident. Thres. −38	Mirr. Dr. T.T. 32
Weight Lift. −40			Mirr. Dr. Er. R. −30	Span of Appreh. −32	
Recogn. −39				Muller-L. Ext. −30	

TABLE 27

FACTOR LOADINGS FOR THE 20–24 RETARDED SAMPLE

Factor I	*Factor II*	*Factor III*	*Factor IV*	*Factor V*	*Factor VI*
Pegboard L. 93	PMA-IQ 73	Ident. Thres. 60	Audio. L. −79	2-Point R. −90	Porteus IQ −70
Pegboard B. 92	PMA-MA 73	Vis. Acuity 57	Audio. R. −78	2-Point L. −72	Porteus MA −69
Pegboard R. 92	Word Assoc. 57	Color Vis. 50	Speech Thres. −48	Muller-L. Antic. 30	Raven −48
Railwalking 74	Grip L. −55	Hand Prec. Er. 39			Azimuth Arith. −46
Scrambled RT. 67	Percep. Speed 47	Recogn. 36			Azimuth Revers. −45
Grip R. 64	Grip R. −47	Span of Appreh. 30			Stereogn. −32
Stereogn. 63	Weight Lift. 35				Mirr. Dr. Er. R. −31
Tapping 62	Atax. L. 34				
Hand Prec. Hits 60	Kinesth. L. 33				
Porteus IQ 59					
Porteus MA 59					
Vis. RT. 58					
Lower Arm 58					
Grip L. 57					
Audio. Choice RT. 57					
PMA-MA 55					
PMA-IQ 55					
Aud. RT. 52					
Raven 52					
Weight Lift. 50					
Recogn. 49					
Hand Prec. Er. 47					
Vis. Acuity 47					
Span of Appreh. 46					
Mirr. Dr. Er. 44					
Azimuth Arith. 42					
Azimuth Rev. 38					
Color Vis. 36					
Percep. Speed 31					

Factor VII	*Factor VIII*	*Factor IX*	*Factor X*	*Factor XI*	*Factor XII*
Time Inter. Est. −47	Mirr. Dr. Er. −72	2-Point R-L −72	Vis. R.T. −64	CFF −57	Kinesth. L. −43
Brightn. Discr. 42	Mirr. Dr. T.T. −56	2-Point L. 45	Aud. R.T. −64	Kinesth. R. 38	Muller-L. Antic. 39
Muller-L. Ext. −41	Mirr. Dr. Er. R. −53	Grip R. 32	Aud. Choice R.T. −38	Atax. L. 35	CA −39
	Lower Arm −34	Grip L. 31	Atax. L . −35		Speech Thres. 38
	Recogn. −32		Scrambled R.T. −35		
			Lower Arm −32		

TABLE 28

Factor Loadings for Normal Sample

Factor I	*Factor II*	*Factor III*	*Factor IV*	*Factor V*	*Factor VI*
PMA-IQ 90	Porteus MA −95	Grip L. −91	Aud. R.T. 82	Atax. L. −75	CFF −53
PMA-MA 81	Porteus IQ −94	Grip R. −89	Vis. R.T. 81	Atax. M. −56	Stereogn. −39
Azimuth Arith. 48	Raven −37	Scrambled R.T. −36	Recogn. 34	Hand Prec. Er. −49	Eye Dom. −38
Percep. Speed 43		Pegboard L. −35	Aud. Choice R.T. 31	Scrambled R.T. −39	Azimuth Arith. −33
Recogn. 42		Muller-L. Antic. −35	Speech Thres. −30	Hand Prec. Hits 37	
Raven 41		Audiom. L. −34		Tapping −36	
Audio. R. 39		CA −33		Aud. Choice R.T. −35	
Lower Arm 35				Railwalking −33	
Brightn. Discr. −30					
Audio. L. 30					

Factor VII	*Factor VIII*	*Factor IX*	*Factor X*	*Factor XI*	*Factor XII*
Hand Dom. −50	Ident. Thresh. −61	2-Point L. −91	Brightn. Disc. −49	Audio. R. −43	Pegboard R. −79
Mirr. Dr. T.T. 48	Vis. Acuity −51	2-Point R-L 48	Speech Thres. −45	Mirr. Dr. Er. R. 31	Pegboard B. −76
Hand Prec. Hits. −35	Kinesth. L. 39	2-Point R. −47	Audio. L. −44	Kinesth. L. 30	Pegboard L. −75
Time Inter. Est. 34		Color Vis. −39	Percep. Speed −42		Tapping −57
Kinesth. R. 32			Muller-L. Antic. 37		Railwalking −53
CA −31			Eye Dom. −32		Hand Prec. Er. −39
					CA −35
					PMA-IQ −33
					PMA-MA −33
					Ident. Thresh. −32
					Span of Appreh. −31
					Atax. M. −31

In keeping with this, and in order to avoid the monotonous task of describing a total of 48 factors, the following discussion was so organized that factors which are common for all four samples or common for the three retarded samples may be considered together for the purpose of interpretation.

The factors are identified by Roman numerals. As before, the four subject samples have been referred to by Arabic numbers from 1 to 4 for the 8-20 retardates, the 12-15 retardates, the 20-24 retardates, and the normals, respectively. A subscript from 1 to 4 following the Roman numeral indicates to which sample the factor refers. Thus I_1 stands for the first factor in the 8-10 retarded sample. Table 29 contains a summary of the interpretations of the factors in the four samples.

TABLE 29

SUMMARY OF THE FACTORS WHICH HAVE BEEN EXTRACTED FROM THE ANALYSIS, AND THE SUBJECT SAMPLES IN WHICH THEY OCCUR

General Ability Factor	I_1	I_2	I_3	XII_4
Intellectual-Perceptual Factor	II_1	VII_2	II_3	I_4
Spatial Related Intellectual Factor	II_1	IX_2	VI_3	II_4
Visual Acuity	X_1	XI_2	III_3	VIII_4
Auditory Acuity	III_1	V_2	IV_3	X_4
Reactive Motor Speed	VIII_1	II_2	X_3	IV_4
Cutaneous Space Discrimination	V_1	III_2	V_3	IX_4
Kinesthesis	XII_1	VIII_2	XII_3	—
Steadiness	VI_1	XII_2	—	V_4
Establishment of Eye-Hand Coordination	VII_1	—	VIII_3	—
Hand Dominance	XI_1	—	—	VII_4
Strength of Grip	—	IV_2	—	III_4
Uninterpretable	IV_1	VI_2	VII_3	VI_4
Uninterpretable	IX_1	X_2	IX_3	XI_4

In all three retarded samples there was a factor which has been interpreted as a *General Ability Factor*: I_1, I_2 and I_3. Characteristic for this factor was that in all retarded samples a great many variables, 24, 31 and 29 respectively, had factor loadings above .30. Twenty-three variables were common for all three samples, and 28 of the 12-15 sample's 31 variables were included in the 29 variables of the oldest sample. In all three samples the lists of variables were headed by the three Pegboard scores. In general, motor variables were found in the upper part of the list, intellectual variables in the middle, and perceptual measures more clustered in the lower part. The three lists differed somewhat with respect to the sequence of the variables. These differences did not have sufficient consistency or magnitude to warrant interpretation, except perhaps that the 12-15 sample had higher loadings for perceptual variables and lower loadings for the RT-tasks. It is interesting, however, to notice that CA had a moderate loading in the youngest sample but was not present in the older samples, which probably reflected the greater importance of a slight age difference in the youngest sample.

Factor XII_4 had a relatively large number of variables and a similar sequence of motor, intellectual, and perceptual variables, as well as CA. It was therefore probably a corresponding factor, even if the extent of its generality did not reach the same proportions as in the retardates. As may be seen in Table 20, factor XII_4 accounted for considerably less variance than did factors I_1, I_2, and I_3. The dominance of a general ability factor in the retardates would seem to be an important difference from normals; e.g., there seemed to be only modest relationship between mental and physical abilities in the normals, contrary to what was found in the retardates. This distinction was in all probability related to the difference in differentiation which was seen in the correlational analysis.

Since Span of Apprehension, Recognition, Weight Lifting, and possibly also Azimuth may be directly related to intelligence level, Factor II_1 may be interpreted as a *General Intelligence* function. In the two older retarded samples this factor was differentiated into an *Intellectual-Perceptual* factor VII_2 and II_3, and a *Spatially Related Intellectual* factor IX_2 and VI_3. The two intellectual factors seemed to be more clearly differentiated in the older than in the 12-15 sample. In the normal sample, also, the two differentiated intellectual factors were found, I_4 and II_4, rather than the general intellectual factor. It may be noted that Raven was included in the Intellectual-Perceptual factor, as well as in the Spatially Related Intellectual factor, in the normals. This may indicate that the perceptual or abstract element of Raven may have primary relevance for the normals, while the more primitive space-relations have more relevance among the retardates.

At the risk of concluding the obvious, we may state that a differentiation of intellectual abilities with age seems to take place at a slower rate in the retardates.

Visual Acuity appeared to be a factor found in all samples: X_1, X_2, III_3, and VIII_4. It was generally represented by Visual Acuity, Color Vision, and ID Threshold.

Auditory Acuity was also found in all four samples: III_1, V_2, IV_3, and X_4 with high loadings on the two pure tone thresholds and speech threshold. In the normal sample, Auditory L but not R was included in the list; in general, it was not as clear a factor here as it was in the retardates. The fact that pure tone thresholds in the retardates had higher factor loadings than had speech threshold may have been a result of the higher interdependency on the two audiometric variables as compared to the normals. In the youngest retarded and in the normal sample, Brightness Discrimination had moderate loadings. This may indicate that the factor has a character of more general sensory discrimination at the younger age levels. Thus this may be an example of differentiation related to age level rather than to mental maturation.

A *Reactive Motor Speed Factor* was also found in all four samples: VIII_1, II_2, X_3, and IV_4. All four reaction times, with the exception of the Scrambled Foreperiod, were included here, but the simple reaction times generally had the highest loadings. This may indicate that Scrambled Foreperiod measures a different function in the normals than in retardates. Emphasis here has been put on reactive motor speed, rather than motor speed as such; since measures like Tapping and Lower Arm, which have the speed element but not the reactive aspects, were poorly represented.

A *Cutaneous Space Discrimination* factor seemed to be present in all four samples: V_1, III_2, I_3, and IX_4. As it was primarily manifested in Two-Point L and R, measures which are not independent, there is some question about this factor.

In the three retarded samples Kinesthesis predominated in XII_1, VIII_2, and XII_3. The interdependence of the two Kinesthesis variables suggests caution. While the factor may be labelled a *Kinesthesis* factor, it cannot be regarded as anything more than a suggestion.

A *Steadiness* factor seemed to be indicated in the two youngest retarded and in the normal sample: V_1, XII_2, and V_4. Only Ataxiometry M and L were common for all three samples, and since these measures are not independent, questions about the factor arose. There were some doubts as to whether this factor should have been interpreted as static steadiness rather than steadiness, to indicate the existence of a dynamic steadiness factor. In the discussion of the overall group comparisons it was suggested that these two factors may be differentiated, particularly in the retardates.

The factors discussed above seemed to be generally found in the four samples, even if the Kinesthesis and Steadiness factors were missing from the normal sample and the oldest retarded sample, respectively. There were a few factors which appeared in but two of the four samples. The first of these was a factor which may be called *Establishment of Eye-Hand Coordination.* It occurred in the youngest and oldest retarded samples, VII_1 and VIII_3, and was dominated by the three Mirror Drawing Scores. Since the scores are interdependent, the question of spuriousness arises. Should the factor be genuine, it may be related to the difference in general performance level.

The youngest retarded and the normal samples may have had a *Hand Dominance* factor, XI_1 and VII_4. Some motor variables had moderate loadings on this factor but the factor was far from clear. It was a bipolar factor in both samples with such suggestive opposites as Speech Threshold for the retardates and Mirror Drawing Total Time and Kinesthesis for the normals. The factor must, however, be regarded as tentative.

Strength of Grip was the dominating feature of IV_2 and III_4. The only additional variable in common in the two samples was CA. That it had a moderate loading on a Strength of Grip factor was not surprising, since it had been noted earlier that strength is the test most closely related to age. It may be noted that Grip was included in the General Ability Factor in all retarded samples, but not in the normals, where the corresponding factor was much more limited. Thus general ability and strength seemed to be more independent functions in the two samples with the highest general performance level, the normals and the 12-15 retardates.

The constellation of variables in VI_2 and IX_3 represented possibly a further differentiation with age of the Cutaneous Space Discrimination factor. Both the 8-10 normals and retardates had Two-Point R-L as the opposite pole in Factors V_1 and IX_4 respectively, while it was absent in the Cutaneous Space Discrimination factor of the older retardates. The tenuousness of the evidence cautions against confidence in this factor.

There were finally, several factors which may be regarded as uninterpretable. These were factors where a constellation of variables or dominating features were found only in one sample and where it was difficult to see the common element of the variables. Such factors were IV_1 and IX_1, suggesting immediate judgement or execution of a task, in the youngest retarded sample; X_2 and XI_2 which may have suggested a quick establishment of perception at the expense of adequate spatial orientation, in the 12-15 sample; VII_3 and XI_3 with possible sensory-perceptual components, in the 20-24 sample; and VI_4 and XI_4, in the normal sample, which were difficult to further specify. There seemed to be a predominance of sensory-perceptual variables in these factors.

Discussion: The overall impression from the factor analysis is of a general similarity of the factor structure for the four samples. With seven factors having appeared in all four samples, the general conclusion must be that the factor structure does not differ substantially between a normal and a retarded sample of the same age, and does not differ greatly between retarded samples of different age levels.

While this appeared as the predominant trend, differences between the samples with respect to factor structure must also be noted. The normals differed from the retardates primarily in that the general factor was not as massive as in the retarded samples. Also the Auditory Acuity and the Cutaneous Space factors were much more dominating in the retarded samples than in the normals. On the other hand, the retardates had considerably less factor loadings than had the normals on the Intellectual-Perceptual, the Spatially Related Intellectual, and possibly also on the Steadiness factors. The Intellectual-Perceptual and the Spatially Related Intellectual factors in the normals did not account for as much variance as did the General Ability Factor in the retardates. In the normals, however, these two factors accounted for more of the variance than they did in the retardates. Delayed differentiation of intellectual abilities was found in the retardates. Other instances of differentiation, independent of mental maturity, were also encountered. Hand Dominance appeared as a factor in the youngest retarded and normal but not in the two older retarded samples, and in the same two younger samples the Auditory Acuity factor tended toward a more general sensory discrimination whereas it was a purer auditory factor in the older samples. It is also of considerable interest to notice that the factors which evolved seemed to be dominated by intellectual, sensory, or motor functions, while perceptual measures never became dominant in a systematic fashion in any factor.

So, while the same factors were found in retardates and normals, their relative significance may differ.

The prevalence in the variables of the General Ability Factor, which was dominated by motor functions, and the emphasis on the Auditory Acuity factor, with particularly high loadings in the audiometric tasks, seemed to support the main findings from the Sample Comparisons; namely, a particular impairment of motor functions and of audiometric measures, which was interpreted to be a result of inadequate alertness functions. The similarity in factor structure in the retardate samples and their difference in emphasis seemed to support the existence of a "Retardate Ability Structure." The dominance of a General Ability factor seems to be consistent with an interpretation of impairment in the retardates of some central function which permeates all tasks, such as deficiency in motivation, attention, or alertness. Such a factor seems also consistent with lack of differentiation of the retardates as discussed under the correlational analysis.

The majority of the factors discussed above were relatively distinct and easy to identify when variables with low loadings and those showing lack of consistency across the samples were disregarded. It appears therefore that there were several basic functions which are clearly specific in retardates as well as in normals. This distinctness is somewhat disturbing since a factor often was reduced to a few interdependent measures obtained with the same test. There may be some question as to whether they actually were factors in the sense in which this term has generally been used in factor analysis. Since they were limited to the specific functions which the test was intended to measure, they took on a different character from ability factors, which should transcend several measures. The relatively heavy emphasis on sensory functions may have resulted from interdependent measures. A follow up with a reduced battery of more independent measures is needed for confirmation or revision of these considerations. The difference found between retardates and normals, however, should be valid, regardless of the question that may be raised about the dependency of some of the measures.

In consideration of the factor analysis, as well as the overall group comparison and the correlation analysis, a reduced version of the test battery may be suggested. Since the content of a test battery always depends upon the purpose for which it is designed, the present remarks are limited to the Ability Structure Project battery when it is used to analyze ability structure in the mentally retardates—particularly as it deviates from normals—and to further define ability factors. On this basis the following tests may be maintained: Hand Dominance, Visual Acuity, Color Vision, Audiometry, Speech Threshold, Two-Point Threshold, Kinesthesis, Ataxiometry, Grip, Lower Arm, Tapping, Auditory RT, Auditory Choice RT, Scrambled Foreperiod RT, Pegboard, Railwalking, Azimuth Arithmetic and Reversals, Apprehension Span, Stereognosis, Recognition, PMA, Porteus, and Raven. Excluded because of low factor loadings, lack of differentiation, or high correlation with other measures, are: Eye Dominance, Visual RT, Hand Precision, Mirror Drawing, Word Association, RT to Pictures, Identification Threshold, Brightness Discrimination, CFF, Time Interval Estimation, Weight Lifting, Muller-Lyer, and Perimetry.

The proposed reduction is particularly heavy for perceptual tests. Hence, in spite of the findings from the present study, it may be advisable to include some additional perceptual tests. Experience with the test battery would suggest that Identification Threshold, RT to Pictures, Time Interval, Brightness Discrimination, and Word Association might be the most promising.

Previous Factor Analytical Studies

Relevant factor analytical studies of retardates are practically non-existent in the literature. McKinney (1962) factor analyzed data obtained by time-sampling observation of the daily behavior of 48 severely retarded boys. Such data can hardly be expected to afford factor interpretations commensurable with those from the ASP data. It is, however, interesting to note that McKinney named his first factor Purposefulness, which seems consistent with the emphasis the present study has placed on response initiation, effort, and ability of the individual to modify his own level of arousal.

Taylor (1964) administered a test battery which included intellectual, perceptual, and manipulation tests, as well as rating on work performance, to 74 subjects in their late teens or early twenties, with a mean IQ of 81. Factor analysis of the correlation matrix resulted in the following interpretable factors: General dexterity, Verbal-numerical-education, Social-vocational competence, Gestalt-perception, Distractability, Mechanical assembly, Fine discrimination, and Filing. The authors commented that the factors were clearly related to those found by other investigators for normal subjects; although the factors tended to be more global than is usual. There are distinct differences between Taylor's list of factors and that of the ASP. Some of these discrepancies are probably related to differences between the test batteries of the two studies and differences in the population samples. While his study does not indicate a dominating general factor, other findings may be more reconcilable. His General dexterity factor may be related to our Motor speed factor; his Verbal numerical-educational factor, to our Intellectual-Perceptual factor; and his Gestalt-perception, to our Spatially Related Intellectual factor.

The most systematic studies of structure of abilities in retardates through factor analysis have been made by Meyers and Dingman and their collaborators. Recently (1964) they presented a thorough discussion of the rationale for factor analysis in mental retardation and reviewed studies which contained hypotheses and corresponding testing programs to verify these factors as well as studies which analyzed existing data. In summarizing their own studies (Meyers et al., 1961, 1962) they stated that factor structure of some theoretical and practical meaningfulness was indicated. While a general intelligence factor was present, they felt that its significance had been overrated, and that such a factor was an insufficient description of young intellects. We cannot take issue with the latter statement, but the ASP data lead us to believe that the significance of a general factor in retardates is profound.

On the basis of previous factor studies in normal adults, Meyers and Dingman (1960) hypothesized the following factor domains for the preschool age: (a.) Psychomotor; whole body (postural balance, dynamic balance, impulsion, coordination, flexibility, strength; (b.) Psychomotor; hand-eye (static precision, dynamic precision, reaction time, dexterity, speed); (c.) Visual Perception (perceptual speed, spatial ability); (d.) Auditory Perception (auditory discrimination-auditory localization); (e.) Receptive Psycholinguistics (auditing, verbal comprehension); (f.) Expressive Psycholinguistics (articulation, semantic fluency, symbolic fluency); and (g.) Mental; memory and thinking (memory span, abstracting, reproduction of visual models). Considering the age difference in the retardates and the limitation of the ASP test battery, there is remarkable similarity between this hypothetical list and the factors found in the retarded samples in the present study.

Meyers and Dingman (1961) compared 100 retarded and 100 normal subjects for the purpose of sampling some primary ability factors which seemed to be well established at adult levels. The retardates did poorest on perceptual speed and reasoning tasks, best on linguistic tasks, with psychomotor tasks occupying the intermediate level. Since the groups were matched for MA, the retarded group was more than twice the age of the normals. Thus the differential maturation age for the various functions was not noted, and the relatively poor motor performance of the retarded not apparent.

Summary

The traditional factor analyses indicated seven factors; General Ability, Intellectual-Perceptual, Spatially Related Intellectual, Visual Acuity, Auditory Acuity, Reactive Motor Speed, and Cutaneous Space Discrimination, which were present in all four samples of this study.

While this may have indicated some degree of similarity in factor structure in normals and retardates of various age ranges, there were clear differences as to the significance of these various factors. There was heavy emphasis on the General Ability factor and some emphasis on the Auditory Acuity factor in the retardates; but less emphasis than was found in the normals on the Intellectual-Perceptual and on the Spatially Related Intelligence factors. Thus the three retarded samples showed an internal consistency which to some extent set them apart from the normals. This seemed to support previous conclusions about a characteristic "Retardate Ability Structure."

Since the General Ability factor was dominated by motor functions, the findings were in accord with previous conclusions concerning particular impairment of motor tasks in the retardates. They concurred also with particular impairment of auditory thresholds, in addition to deficiency in general intelligence and motor functions, and with the lack of differentiation which was indicated in the correlation analysis. Again, it seemed indicated that the impaired functions affected, to greater or lesser extent, almost all of the tasks of the retardates.

Thus the findings from the traditional factor analysis seemed to be in accord with the main findings from the Sample Comparisons and the Correlation Analysis.

INVERSE FACTOR ANALYSIS

With the same computer program as for the traditional factor analysis, 15 factors were extracted from the correlation matrix between individuals, and 12 of these factors were rotated to simple structure by the quartimax procedure.[7] This was done for each of the four samples. The rotated subject factors (SF) are identified by Arabic numbers to prevent confusion with the factors resulting from the traditional factor analysis, where the test factors have been referred to by Roman numbers. The purpose of the inverse factor analysis was to determine if specific subgroups of retardates could be defined on the basis of the 50 variables in the test battery, and if such groups would be similar to subject groups in the normal sample. The computer program could not accommodate a correlation matrix larger than 70 x 70 and for this reason Samples 2, 3 and 4 were limited to 70 subjects, while all the 68 subjects of Sample 1 were included. The basis for exclusion was incomplete scores, supplemented by low examiner rating, until 70 subjects were left.

Factor variances for the four samples are listed in Table 30. This table shows that except for SF1 no factor contributed more than 7.9% of the total variance. Also, the 15 SFs combined did not contribute more than 70% of the variance in the retardates and 66% in the normals. From these two observations it might have been concluded that

[7] The tables of factor loadings for the four samples separately may be obtained from American Documentation Institute.

TABLE 30

FACTOR VARIANCE FOR THE FOUR INVERSE FACTOR ANALYSES

	Factor Variances			
No.	8–10	12–15	20–24	Normals
1	.1935	.1861	.1923	.1579
2	.0592	.0776	.0788	.0723
3	.0682	.0553	.0450	.0584
4	.0434	.0479	.0504	.0538
5	.0450	.0480	.0452	.0430
6	.0439	.0460	.0398	.0376
7	.0327	.0326	.0380	.0326
8	.0342	.0343	.0321	.0377
9	.0307	.0302	.0282	.0297
10	.0336	.0309	.0279	.0282
11	.0276	.0280	.0282	.0280
12	.0224	.0226	.0261	.0196
13	.0202	.0199	.0218	.0235
14	.0206	.0231	.0200	.0198
15	.0222	.0179	.0197	.0198
Total	.6974	.7003	.6936	.6620

our subjects were not falling into a few well defined subgroups. The same trend was indicated in the distribution of subjects according to the factor where they had the highest loading. This distribution is presented in Table 31. For several SFs there were too few individuals to constitute a meaningful subgroup of subjects. In all retarded samples there were substantially more subjects clustered in SF1 than in any other factor. The normals had a more even distribution of subjects over the factors. It should be noted that in this respect the oldest retarded sample was as close to the normals as it was to the other retarded samples.

TABLE 31

NUMBER OF SUBJECTS EXHIBITING HIGHEST LOADING ON THE ROTATED FACTORS

Factor	*8–10*	*12–15*	*20–24*	*Normals*
1	29	25	17	9
2	6	3	14	14
3	4	4	3	7
4	4	8	5	6
5	3	5	5	4
6	3	3	5	2
7	3	2	3	4
8	5	5	2	6
9	3	2	6	8
10	4	4	2	3
11	1	5	2	4
12	3	4	6	3

To aid in the interpretation of the subject factors, graphic and correlational procedures were utilized. For each factor, group means were computed for all 50 variables, including the subjects who had the highest loading on the factor, and, as a subsequent attempt, including all subjects who had a factor loading above .30 on the factor. Positive and negative factor loadings had to be considered separately. The resulting group means were then plotted, so that profiles for each SF (positive and negative) were obtained. This proved to be an exceedingly difficult way of ascertaining the characteristics of the various subgroups. In the multiplicity of variables, it was impossible to single out simply by inspection the variables which in a meaningful way identified the various groups.

Another way of determining which variables were associated with factors was to compute their correlations with factor loadings. The variables with high correlations serve to characterize SF (Bolduc, 1960; Guthrie, Butler, and Gorlow, 1961; Culbertson, Guthrie, Butler, and Gorlow, 1961).

The interpretation of the subject factors on the basis of correlations between factor loadings and variables was also a very difficult proposition for several reasons. In the first place, there were many SFs where only a small number of subjects represented the factor, whether subjects were counted by the highest loading (as was seen from Table 31) or by loading above .30. Secondly, there was little resemblance between factors of the four samples. A comparison of the variables which had a high correlation with the factor loadings showed that only SF 1 had any similarity across retarded samples. In a few other instances, a similarity was indicated but was found to be limited to a maximum of four common variables and a constellation which defied interpretation. A third reason was that an attempt to interpret 12 subject factors from each sample proved to be more confusing than enlightening, as the differences between factors within a sample were often difficult to determine; particularly so, since one had to consider positive and negative loadings on each factor separately, which might have increased the number of groups to 24 in each sample. These were compelling reasons for limiting the factor interpretation to a few selected factors. Accordingly, the factors were selected where more than 5 subjects had their highest loading. Table 31 indicates that factors 1_1, 2_1, 1_2, 4_2, 1_3, 2_3, 9_3, 12_3, 1_4, 2_4, 3_4, 4_4, 8_4, and 9_4 fulfilled this criterion. Correlations between variables and factor loadings have been limited to these 14 SFs listed in Table 32. The entries include correlation coefficients above .30 which corresponds very closely to the 1% level of confidence.

In all three retarded samples *Factor 1* deviated clearly from the other factors in two aspects: more subjects had their highest loading on this factor than on any other, and correlations above .30 were found for a large number of variables. Of 31 variables which reached criterion correlations in SF 1, 26 variables reached this level in the 12-15 sample. Similarly, of 29 such variables in the oldest retarded sample, 23 reached the criterion for the 12-15 sample. The same 23 variables were common for all three retarded samples. Thus it might be concluded that an SF which occurred in all three retarded samples had been identified. It was a bipolar factor, since positive as well as negative loadings existed, but the correlations between variables and factor loadings had uniform signs. For the purpose of interpretation, it may be observed that all types of variables were included—perhaps less sensory tasks than others. It appeared therefore that the characteristic of this subgroup was the overall ability level and that it might be named the General Ability Group. The variables which characterized this group showed considerable relationship to the General Ability Factor found in the traditional factor analysis, in that a set of 20 variables were found to be common in all three retarded samples.

In spite of the difficulty found in distinguishing factors by graphic means, one can compare the characteristic profiles of the three samples on a common factor. Accordingly, the 23 variables common for the General Ability SF in the thre retarded samples were plotted separately for subjects with positive and negative loadings in Fig. 7. Included in the figure is the profile for SF 2_4 of the normal sample, as this was the factor which most closely resembled the General Ability SF of the retardates. It appears from the figure that the groups with negative loadings in the normal and in the youngest retarded sample corresponded to the groups with positive loadings in the two older samples because of similarity in profile and level. Conversely, groups with positive loadings from the normal and youngest retarded samples corresponded to the groups with negative loadings of the two older samples. It was these groups which constituted the major differences between factors in the three retarded samples. These differences can most readily be seen in the motor measures: Lower Arm Movement and the RTs, primarily in the youngest sample. It is also of note that the positively loaded group of the youngest retarded sample had a much larger *N* than the corresponding negatively loaded groups of the older samples. Although positive and negative loadings were found in the normal sample, their profiles showed little resemblance to those of the retardates.

TABLE 32a

CORRELATION COEFFICIENTS ABOVE .30 BETWEEN VARIABLES AND FACTOR LOADINGS FROM THE INVERSE FACTOR ANALYSIS

SF 1_1	SF 2_1	SF 1_2	SF 4_2	SF 1_3
Span of Appreh. −75	Audio. L. 67	PMA-MA 73	Atax. L. −51	Porteus IQ 74
Pegboard B. −74	Mirr. Dr. T.T. −59	Pegboard B. 67	Brightn. Discr. −47	Porteus MA 73
Pegboard L. −74	Audio. R. 51	Pegboard R. 66	Muller-L. Ext. 43	Raven 68
Porteus MA −73	Mirr. Dr. Er. −48	Railwalking 66	Weight Lift. −43	Stereogn. 65
PMA-MA −73	Brightn. Discr. 47	Azimuth Arith. 66	Color Vis. 40	Pegboard L. 65
Porteus IQ −70	Kinesth. L. −43	Porteus MA 65	Hand Prec. H. 37	Pegboard R. 64
Raven −69	Kinesth. R. −42	Pegboard L. 63	Porteus IQ 33	Pegboard B. 64
Pegboard R. −69	2-Point R. −33	Stereogn. 62	Porteus MA 32	Azimuth Rev. 63
Azimuth Arith. −65	PMA-IQ 32	Recogn. 62	Kinesth. R. −31	Recogn. 60
Scrambled R.T. −63		Vis. R.T. 61	2-Point R. −31	Scrambled R.T. 58
Vis. R.T. −62		Porteus IQ 60	Time Int. Est. 30	Railwalking 57
Azimuth Rev. −62		PMA-IQ 59	Mirr. Dr. Er. R. 30	Aud. Choice R.T. 57
Aud. R.T. −61		Span of Appreh. 58	Aud. Choice R.T. 30	Mirr. Dr. Er. 55
PMA-IQ −58		Raven 57		Lower Arm 53
Vis. Acuity −56		Scrambled R.T. 54		Aud. R.T. 51
Railwalking −56		Lower Arm 53		Azimuth Arith. 49
Tapping −56		Percep. Speed 53		Hand Prec. Er. 44
Stereogn. −55		Vis. Acuity 51		Tapping 43
Aud. Choice R.T. −51		Azimuth Rev. 52		PMA-MA 40
Lower Arm −51		Hand Prec. Er. 51		PMA-IQ 40
Recogn. −49		Tapping 51		Kinesth. L. 39
Kinesth. L. −47		Aud. R.T. 50		Vis. R.T. 38
Hand Prec. H. −45		Mirr. Dr. Er. 49		Kinesth. R. 37
Kinesth. R. −44		Aud. Choice R.T. 48		Time Inter. Est. 37
Atax. L. −42		Color Vis. 39		Span of Appreh. 37
Hand Prec. Er. −41		Atax. M. 33		Mirr. Dr. Er. R. 36
Mirr. Dr. Er. −37		CFF 31		Visual Acuity 35
CFF −34				Weight Lift. −33
Atax. M. −32				Hand Prec. H. 32
Audio. R. −31				
Color Vis. −30				

TABLE 32b

SF 2_3	SF 9_3	SF 12_3	SF 1_4	SF 2_4
PMA MA 75	Muller-L. Ext. −55	Percep. Speed −57	Pegboard R. 78	PMA MA −66
PMA IQ 75	Atax. M. −45	Scrambled RT −43	Pegboard B 74	Aud. RT −61
Word Assoc. 63	Word Assoc. −42	Word Assoc. −42	Railwalking 63	Vis. RT −60
Tapping 56	Eye Dom. −35	Vis. Acuity 35	Atax. M 61	Scrambled RT −57
Atax. L 56	Time Inter. Est. −32	Mir. Dr. Er. 34	Pegboard L 60	Azim. Arith. −56
Scrambled RT 54		PMA IQ −33	Ident. Thresh. 51	Tapping −53
Weight Lift. 53		PMA MA −33	Audio. L. 49	Pegboard B −52
Railwalking 51			PMA MA 48	Porteus MA −52
Aud. Choice RT 50			Span of Appreh. 47	Recogn. −51
Pegboard L 50			Raven 46	Mir. Dr. Er. −49
Percep. Speed 46			Tapping 46	Aud. Choice RT −49
Pegboard B 46			Porteus MA 44	Lower Arm −47
Pegboard R 44			Muller-L Ext. −42	Pegboard L −46
Aud. RT 44			Porteus IQ 40	PMA IQ −46
Hand Prec. Er. 43			PMA IQ 39	Raven −45
Mir. Dr. T.T. 43			CFF −38	Pegboard R −43
2-Point L −40			Percep. Speed 38	Percep. Speed −42
Recogn. 39			Audio. R. 38	Atax. M. −41
Azimuth Rev. 38			Weight Lift. −36	Porteus IQ −39
Audio. L. 38			2-Point R 36	Hand Prec. Er. −38
Kinesth. R. 36			Speech Thres. 32	Atax. L. −37
Vis. Acuity 34			Mir. Dr. Er. 32	Azimuth Rev. −33
Span of Appreh. 34			2-Point L 32	Word Assoc. −33
Audio. R. 33			Stereogn. 30	Audio. L. −31
2-Point R-L 32				Stereogn. −31
Color Vis. 30				

TABLE 32c

SF 3_4	SF 4_4	SF 8_4	SF 9_4
Hand Prec. Er. 59	Hand Dom. −51	Muller-L. Antic −54	PMA-MA −72
Percep. Speed −49	Time Inter. Est. −44	Vis. Acuity −53	Pegboard L. −58
Ident. Thresh. −48	Pegboard L. 41	Pegboard L. −53	PMA-IQ −54
Raven −44	Vis. R.T. −41	Scrambled RT −49	Railwalking −54
Atax. L. 43	Word Assoc. 41	2-Point L. −47	Pegboard R −49
Eye Dom. −36	Aud. R.T. −39	2-Point R. −44	Pegboard B −48
PMA-IQ −36	Kinesth. R. 36	Pegboard Both −37	2-Point R −48
Aud. Choice R.T. −32	2-Point L. 35	Span of Appreh −37	Tapping −47
Stereogn. −31	2-Point R. 34	Audio. L. −36	Audio. R. −46
Muller-L. Ext. −31	Atax. M. −32	Mir. Dr. Er. R. −35	Audio. L. −43
Audio. R. −30	Porteus MA 32	Ident. Thres. −35	Brightn. Discr. 36
Recogn. −30	Audio. R. 31	Mir. Dr. T.T. −34	Color Vis. 35
2-Point R. −30		Hand Dom. 32	Lower Arm −35
		Time Inter. Est. 32	Hand Prec. Err. −34
		Recogn. −31	Azimuth Arith. −31
		Eye Dom. 31	
		Railwalking −30	

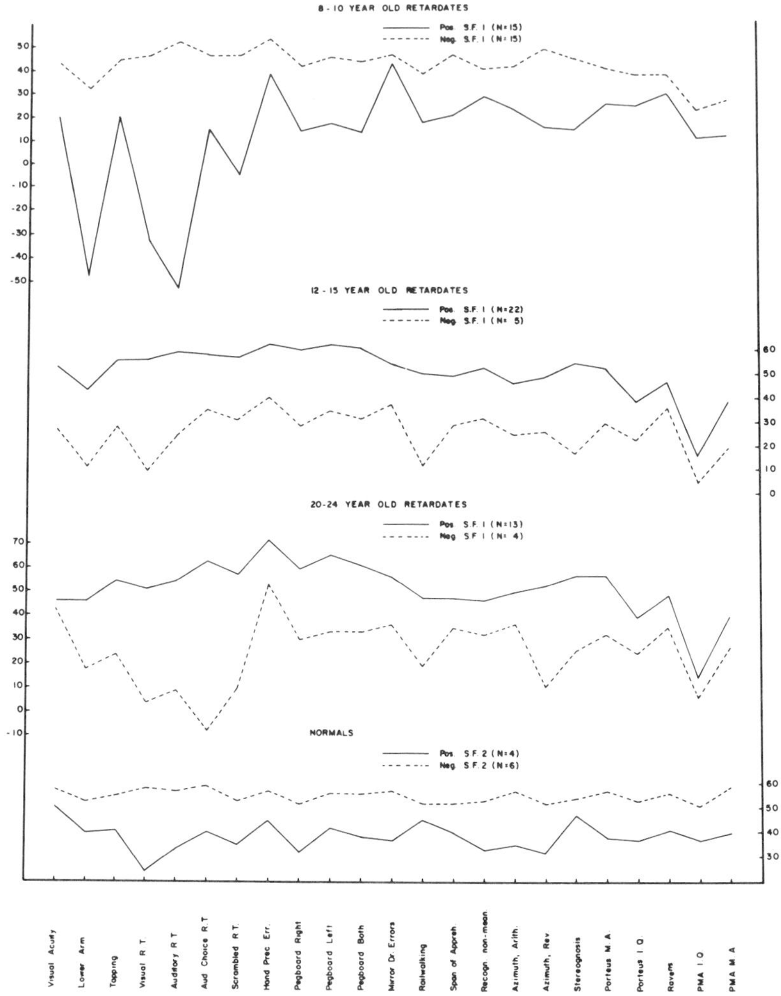

Figure 7. The 23 variables which the three samples have in common for the General Ability factor, plotted in terms of *T* scores for positive and negative factors separately.

The bipolar factors $SF\ 2_1$ seemed related to some sensory variables; with positive correlation to Auditory threshold; negative, to Kinesthesis and Two-Point Threshold. Mirror Drawing Total Time and Error—variables which had presented problems in interpretation—had negative correlations, while Brightness Discrimination and PMA-IQ had positive correlations. This was a difficult factor to interpret, and, since none of the factors in the other retarded samples had a reasonable similarity to it, it must be concluded that it was a questionable factor for use in defining a subgroup. No test factor (TF) appeared to be similar to this SF.

It appears then that in the youngest retarded sample only one subject group was clearly defined; namely, the General Ability Group.

In the 12-15 retarded sample, SF 4_2 was a bipolar factor which showed negative correlations with Ataxiometer L, Brightness Discrimination, Muller-Lyer Extent, Kinesthesis R, and Two-Point R; and positive correlation with Weight Lifting, Color Vision, Hand Precision Hits, Porteus IQ and MA, and with Time Interval Estimation. Positive correlations involved evaluation of spatial, weight, and temporal relationships while the negative correlations were more concerned with sensory functions, particularly proprioceptive function. Brightness Discrimination and Muller-Lyer, however, did not fit into this pattern. The factor must be regarded with extreme caution. It may be noted that a TF with a similar list of variables was not found. Whereas a subject group, characterized by contrasting spatial, weight, and temporal relationships to sensory functions was indicated, only the General Ability Group was positively identified in the 12-15 year old retarded sample.

In the oldest retarded sample, three additional factors were considered. *SF* 2_3, having almost uniformly positive correlations, was particularly characterized by intellectual functions (PMA), Word Association, motor speed, and motor coordination measures. Sensory and perceptual measures were represented, but in general had lower correlations. The factor may thus be called an *Intellectual-Motor* factor. It had several variables in common with TFs II_3 and X_3 and—while neither alone wholly corresponded to this factor—combined, they made a fair approximation. *SF* 9_3 had positive correlation to Muller-Lyer Extent, and negative correlations to Ataxiometer M, Word Association, Eye Dominance and Time Interval Estimation. Only the positive factor was above .50, indicating that the factor was not a powerful one. What the variables with negative signs had in common is difficult to see, particularly with positive signs for extent of Muller-Lyer Illusion. Hence, the factor may be regarded as uninterpretable. None of the TFs showed close relationship to this SF even though VII_3 included Time Interval Estimation and Muller-Lyer Extent with opposite signs.

Subject Factor 12_3 had negative correlation with RT to Pictures (Perceptual Speed), Scrambled RT, Word Association, PMA-IQ and -MA and positive correlation with Visual Acuity and Mirror Drawing Error. There appeared to be a perceptual element common to the variables with negative correlations; possibly speed of perception. There was a reasonable similarity to TF II_3, which was called an Intellectual-Perceptual factor, but since the emphasis was reversed, the present SF might be called a *Perceptual-Intellectual* factor. Thus, in the oldest retarded sample, two subject factors—an Intellectual-Motor and a Perceptual-Intellectual factor—were indicated in addition to the General Ability factor.

An additional way of searching for factors may be to use as guides the factors from the traditional factor analysis which were presented in Table 25. By this method other factors were identified with more or less clarity. An Auditory factor was made up by SFs 4_1, 2_2, and 7_3; a Cutaneous Space Discrimination factor of 5_1, 11_2, and 5_3; and a Kinesthesis factor of 2_1, 8_2, and 3_3. Since so few subjects had their highest loading on these factors, their main importance may be to lend weight to the test factors. In particular, inspection of the profiles of the individuals in the Auditory SF seemed to bear out the interpretation that they had impairment of pure tone threshold in accordance with magnitude and sign of the factor loading. Some of the other test factors may also have been linked to SF but the relationships seemed to be sporadic. Thus, while some TFs were found also as SFs, little was gained toward defining subgroups by this attempt.

The normal sample had two factors where many variables had correlations above .30 with the factor loadings: SFs 1_4 and 2_4, with 14 variables in common. While both had the character of a General Factor, SF 1_4 had less of a reactive motor component. It may most properly be called *General Ability Factor A,* but it should be noted that it did not correspond closely to the General Ability factor which was found in the retardates. The variables involved seemed to be a combination of TFs I_4, II_4, and XII_4.

SF 2_4 may then be called *General Ability Factor B* and seemed to be more comparable to the General Ability factor of the retardates, as it had relatively more emphasis on reactive motor components. Consequently, this factor was included in Fig. 7. In some aspects, the factor appeared to be the negative counterpart to SF 1_4, but the heavier emphasis on reactive speed made it appear as a separate factor. It seemed to have elements from several TFs: I_4, II_4, IV_4, and XII_4, although none were represented in full. It is important to note that, in contrast to findings among the retardates, there was only a small portion of the normals who made up this factor.

SF 3_4 had negative correlations to a series of measures from which motor variables were conspicuously absent. There was suggestion of a "mental speed" or a perceptual speed that characterized this factor.

The positive correlations to Hand Precision Errors and Ataxiometry were not readily understandable in this connection. The naming of the factor had to remain indeterminate. The factor could not be described in terms of a single TF or a simple combination of TFs. It would be interesting if the trend of this factor should be verified by further investigation of normal subjects.

Negative correlations to hand dominance, time perception, motor speed, sway, and positive correlations to finger coordination, speed of verbal production, kinesthesis, Two-Point Threshold, Porteus MA, and Audiometry R, characterized *SF* 4_4. This was an assortment of sensory functions contrasted by laterality, reactive speed, and sway. While a pattern of the variables was indicated, the organization did not seem sufficiently firm to allow positive identification. No one TF accounted for this combination of measures: TF VII_4 contributed most heavily, but variables from several other TFs were included as well.

Negative correlations were consistently found for *SF* 8_4. There was, however, such a curious conglomeration of sensory, motor, and perceptual tasks, that it was a difficult factor to make sense of and must therefore be left uninterpreted. It did not correspond to any specific TF. In conclusion: it must be regarded as questionable whether this factor represented a subgroup of normal subjects.

A similar predominance of negative correlations was found for *SF* 9_4. The variables involved were intellectual, motor coordination of all levels, cutaneous space discrimination, and pure tone threshold. The first two dominated the factor and it might therefore be called a *Motor Coordination-Intellectual* factor. It differed from SF 2_4 by emphasizing motor coordination rather than motor speed. Several of these variables appeared in TF XII_4 with elements from some other TFs.

In addition to determining characteristics of the subgroups by correlating variables and factor loadings, it was of interest to explore the differences between the groups in terms of Mean *T* score, *T* score *SD*, MA and IQ. These data for the 14 subgroups of individuals with factor loadings above .30 are presented in Table 33 with separate listing for those with positive and negative loadings. The General Ability factor (SF 1) in the three retarded samples showed a distinct difference between positive and negative subgroups for all four measures, as did the Intellectual-Motor factor SF 2_3. In the youngest retarded sample the negative subgroup had the higher performance level, whereas the positive subgroups in the other three samples had the higher performance level. Thus the General Ability groups in the re-

TABLE 33

MEANS FOR FOUR QUANTITATIVE VARIABLES FOR GROUPS OF SUBJECTS HAVING FACTOR LOADINGS OF .30 AND ABOVE ON SELECTED FACTORS EVOLVING FROM INVERSE FACTOR ANALYSIS

	Subject Factors		*N*	*Mean T score*	*T score S.D.*	*M.A.*	*I.Q.*
8–10							
	Factor 1	Positive	22	27.0	28.2	57	51
		Negative	19	43.0	14.1	79	66
	Factor 2	Positive	4	37.5	14.9	69	67
		Negative	8	32.1	27.2	58	48
12–15							
	Factor 1	Positive	29	49.7	13.9	100	59
		Negative	6	33.1	16.9	70	45
	Factor 4	Positive	7	46.7	14.2	88	54
		Negative	2	43.3	14.1	93	54
20–24							
	Factor 1	Positive	22	49.2	15.2	100	55
		Negative	6	30.7	21.7	74	41
	Factor 2	Positive	19	47.8	14.9	113	63
		Negative	5	29.9	22.2	66	37
	Factor 9	Positive	4	42.1	14.9	83	46
		Negative	4	43.5	18.6	91	50
	Factor 12	Positive	4	41.7	20.5	83	46
		Negative	3	42.2	18.3	93	52
Normals							
	Factor 1	Positive	11	53.3	9.3	126	117
		Negative	6	44.0	10.2	98	97
	Factor 2	Positive	8	44.8	11.2	99	92
		Negative	17	54.0	8.5	137	122
	Factor 3	Positive	7	49.4	9.7	110	101
		Negative	5	52.2	9.9	126	119
	Factor 4	Positive	8	51.8	9.2	125	112
		Negative	1	51.0	6.9	118	111
	Factor 8	Positive	1	43.1	10.6	97	101
		Negative	11	52.2	8.5	122	108
	Factor 9	Positive	4	46.8	9.1	94	90
		Negative	10	53.2	9.2	139	121

tarded samples and the Intellectual-Motor group in the 20-24 sample were split into subgroups of generally high and generally low performance. The difference in corresponding subgroups across the three samples with respect to Mean *T* score may be accounted for by age, and by the selective sampling discussed in a previous section.

Positive and negative subgroups of SF 2_1 showed moderate difference for Mean *T* score, and probably also for MA, while they had considerable difference for *T* score *SD* and IQ. The group with the poorest performance was somewhat older, which accounts for the difference between MA and IQ. For the remaining SFs among the retardates there was little difference between positive and negative subgroups.

Thus it appeared that the best defined groups among the retardates had characteristically a marked difference between positive and negative subgroups with respect to the overall tendencies which were being measured by Mean *T* score, *T* score *SD*, MA, and IQ.

Similar differences between positive and negative subgroups as were found in the retardates were noted for normals, except for SFs 3_4 and 4_4. Among the subgroups of the normals there was hardly any difference for across-test variability (*T* score *SD*), and there was not always consistency for Mean *T* score, MA, and IQ. Also there was less difference between the subgroups of the normal sample than was found among the retardates. It appeared then that Mean *T* score, *T* score *SD*, MA, and IQ had less supportive value in defining subgroups among normals than among retardates.

Because of the small *N* in each of the retarded subgroups there was limited value in commenting upon the etiological composition, neurological findings, and EEG pattern in each of them. It was possible, however, to explore these variables by pooling the individuals in the three General Ability groups, and to contrast high and low performance level subjects (positive and negative loadings). Since the total number of subjects in the two categories were 70 and 34 respectively, the distributions over the various clinical categories have been expressed as percentage in Table 34.

TABLE 34

HIGH PERFORMANCE AND LOW PERFORMANCE GROUPS OF THE GENERAL ABILITY GROUP AS THEY ARE DISTRIBUTED OVER CATEGORIES OF ETIOLOGY, EEG, AND NEUROLOGICAL IMPAIRMENT

	High Performance Level (%)	*Low Performance Level (%)*
Etiology		
Familials	14	6
Organics	40	62
Unexplained	20	3
Mixed	14	18
Mongoloids	0	9
Not Differentiated	12	3
Degree of EEG Abnormality		
Normal	43	21
Borderline	29	29
Occ. Abnormal	6	6
Abnormal	21	44
Overall Neurological Signs		
Normal	79	44
Slight Impairment	17	29
Severe Impairment	1	26

With regard to etiology it is interesting to note that in general all etiological categories were represented in both the high and low performance subgroups of the General Ability group. Thus there was not a strong relationship between etiological categories and subgroups as they were defined by inverse factor analysis. It seemed, however, that the group with the higher performance level had slightly more Familials, less Organics (even if this was the largest category), more Unexplained, fewer Mongoloids, and more Not Classifiable, than the group with the lower performance level. Thus a trend in the direction of the traditional association between organic etiology and low performance level was suggested. Similarly, the high performance group had twice as many subjects with normal EEG and half as many with abnormal EEG as had the low performance group. The higher incidence of abnormal EEG was distributed over the categories of seizure activity, slow frequency, and unstable rhythm.

The overall neurological signs showed higher incidence of slight and severe impairment in the low performance group than in the high performance group.

It thus appeared that the General Ability group of the retardates was a bipolar factor where one pole attracted the individuals who had a higher general performance level, less across-trait variability, higher MA and IQ, less organic etiology, and less EEG and neurological impairment than had the individuals who were clustered around the opposite pole.

Discussion

The inverse factor analysis was not a productive procedure in defining subgroups of retardates. A large proportion of the retardates belonged to a General Ability subgroup, and this was the only subgroup which could be identified with any degree of certainty among the retardates. It may be asked if this rather negative outcome resulted from the inadequacy of the inverse factor analysis to define subgroups, or if it was the reflection of genuine characteristics of the retardates. It may be noted that other investigators have experienced difficulties in using inverse factor analysis with a retarded population (e.g., Bolduc, 1960; Guthrie et al., 1961; Culbertson et al., 1961). This could have been due to technical problems in the rotating procedures, or it could have reflected the difficulties involved in fractionating a retarded population into subgroups. There were indications that the latter was the case. The normals differed from the retardates, particularly from the younger retardates, in that a smaller proportion belonged to the General Ability group. Several additional subgroups were suggested which are reasonably interpretable, some with considerable representation. The finding of more distinctive subgroups among the normals than among the retardates indicated that the statistical procedure was not the limitation in the defining of subgroups. Also, in the oldest retarded sample a smaller part of the population belonged to the General Ability group while other subgroups were correspondingly better represented. While these subgroups were not well defined, the trend seemed to be toward greater distinction of subgroups in the adult retardates, possibly as a developmental trend. The first two SFs in the oldest retarded sample resembled the first two SFs in the normal sample. Both factors in the two samples were of rather general nature, but the second factor (SF 2_3 and 2_4) had more emphasis on motor functions. If additional subgroups existed among the retardates, they included so few individuals that it was impossible to identify the special characteristics. Thus they were without practical significance.

The finding of less distinctive subgroups in the retardates than in the normals seemed to be at variance with the rather prevalent view in the area of mental retardation that the retardates present characteristic behavioral symptoms and constellations of abilities in accordance with etiological classification. The finding was more consistent with some of our previous results. It was consistent with our notion of a characteristic ability profile for retardates, and with the lack of difference between etiological categories previously reported. The finding was probably related to lack of differentiation in the retardates, as discussed under Correlation Analysis, and to the heavy emphasis in the retarded samples on the General Ability factor as seen from the Traditional Factor Analysis.

Most of the variables in Fig. 7 which differentiated between positive and negative loadings of the General Ability SF belonged to the domain of motor and complex mental functions. Since they, in general, were the same variables which differentiated between normals and retardates, this indicated that here we were dealing with different degrees of retardation rather than different kinds. The difference in level of the Mean *T* score and the IQ variables in Table 29 supported this. Table 29 also indicated that there was less relationship of overall ability level and across-trait variability to IQ in the normals than in the retardates. This was consistent with the higher correlations between complex mental and other variables in the retardates as compared to the normals.

Summary

The general conclusion from the inverse factor analysis seems to be that a definite case for functionally determined subgroups of mentally retarded subjects is difficult to make. In the retardates only a General Ability group with positive and negative factor loadings was identified. This group, however, seemed to be well established, both with regard to confidence of interpretation and to number of subjects included. The characteristic traits of this group seemed to be related to the General Ability factor as determined by the traditional factor analysis. In the oldest retardates a second subgroup (Perceptual-Intellectual) was indicated.

In contrast to the retardates, four subgroups were identified in the normal sample. One of them was a General Ability group corresponding to what has been found for the retardates, but it did not dominate the sample.

These findings do not concur with the notion that etiological categories have distinct behavioral characteristics. They do, however, support our previous interpretations of a mentally retarded ability structure, of no difference between etiological groups, and of less differentiation in the retardates.

It was found that positive and negative loadings on the General Ability factor corresponded to generally high and generally low level of functioning. Motor and complex mental functions, more than sensory and perceptual functions, differentiated between these levels.

SYNDROME ANALYSIS

Because of poor identification of subgroups by inverse factor analysis, an additional statistical approach was adopted in attempting to fractionate the three retarded subject samples into homogeneous groups. Several statistical techniques were considered for the additional analysis, such as Cronbach and Gleser's (1953) profile analysis, McQuitty's cluster analysis (1961), and the procedure developed by Zubin, Fleiss, and Burdock (1962). In the absence of any rational way of comparing the various techniques, practical considerations prevailed and Saunders' Syndrome Analysis was chosen. As a supplement to inverse factor analysis which is based on correlation, syndrome analysis has the advantage of considering profile level. While a description of the procedures has not yet been published, it was discussed by Saunders and Schucman at the Psychonomic Society Meeting (1962) and an application of the technique was presented by

Schucman, Saunders, and Thetford at the American Psychological Association Meeting (1962). Saunders has developed a computer program of the syndrome analysis for the IBM 709 computer and has provided the analysis of the present data. On the basis of Saunders' paper the procedure may be described as follows: the first step is to determine a matrix of relations between individuals. In this case distance measured (distance squared) has been preferred over a correlation measure, since the latter irretrievably removes any contribution of profile level from the analysis. "The second step in a syndrome analysis is to derive a set of clusters from the distance matrix (or its equivalent). Fortunately, it can be sufficient . . . to isolate point clusters—what we call 'nodes'."

The computational technique utilized for finding nodes

> . . . is one which searches for all possible nodes in parallel, and begins by regarding every individual in the sample as a cluster of order one. With each pass of the distance matrix the best addition of one case is made to each cluster. After each pass the members of each enlarged cluster are sorted in order, and the list of clusters is examined for duplication. The maximum frequency for any cluster is equal to the number of members in the cluster, but this frequency will be achieved only if each and every member of the cluster may be used as a starting point for building it up. Such a cluster may be called a 'closed cluster', and is worthy of further attention as a possible node.
>
> The search for closed clusters may theoretically be continued until the entire sample has been brought into every cluster, but this is not necessary in practice. Experience suggests that the process may be safely terminated after five consecutive passes of the distance matrix have yielded no more closed clusters. When this point is reached, it is now only necessary to examine the list of closed clusters, eliminating those which are contained in larger closed clusters that come to light later in the search process. The resulting list of non-overlapping closed clusters may be regarded as a list of nodes for the given distance matrix.
>
> The third step in a syndrome analysis is to characterize the nodes. This may involve nothing more than finding a mean profile for the individuals who have been aggregated, or it may involve construction of the within-node variance-covariance matrix of test scores.
>
> The fourth and ultimate step in a syndrome analysis is to provide a summary, accounting for each individual in the original sample. In its most rudimentary form this will simply be a matrix of distances from individuals to syndromes, with any intra-syndrome variability ignored.

Saunders observed that one of the essential features of Syndrome Analysis technique is "that they proceed without recourse to any a priori information as to the proper assignment of individuals to groups, or even as to the number of groups to be recognized."

The number of subjects included in the nodal groups (Original NG) for the four population samples of the present study is shown in Table 35. The table shows that very few nodes contained as many as five subjects. While significance tests for syndrome analysis are not available, Saunders offered as guide-post that for samples of thirty or more cases involving ten-dimensional input, the largest node may by chance contain as many as four or five cases. It was difficult to trans-

TABLE 35

NUMBER OF SUBJECTS, GROUP MEANS FOR MEAN *T* SCORE, AND *T* SCORE *SD* FOR NODAL GROUPS (MEAN *T* SCORE AND *T* SCORE *SD* IN NORMALS ARE FOR ORIGINAL RATHER THAN EXTENDED NGS)

	NG#	*Original NG N*	*Extend NG N*	*Mean T Score*	*T Score SD*	*PMA IQ*	*PMA MA*
8–10 Ret.	1	17	24	42.3	14.6	67	76
	2	5	18	30.4	23.0	51	59
	3	5	18	28.0	31.4	53	59
	4	3	3	29.9	29.3	52	64
12–15 Ret.	1	8	20	43.2	19.8	51	84
	2	4	12	50.0	12.5	61	101
	3	4	7	43.0	13.2	57	91
	4	3	6	29.6	31.5	39	63
	5	3	6	49.5	13.6	55	96
	6	3	5	46.6	14.6	53	85
	7	3	11	40.1	15.3	49	82
	8	3	7	34.0	17.4	44	67
20–24 Ret.	1	4	9	48.6	13.7	55	100
	2	3	43	33.2	24.8	40	71
	3	3	9	48.2	13.8	57	102
	4	3	14	47.2	16.7	61	109
				Original NG			
Normal	1	5	—	51.7	7.9	114	126
	2	4	—	49.8	8.0	120	128
	3	3	—	53.1	7.9	120	130
	4	3	—	47.3	7.9	111	107

late this to the present situation with two to three times as many subjects.

For the purpose of interpreting the subgroups, so-called extended nodal groups were formed since the *N*s of the original nodal groups were so small. An extended nodal group consisted of the actual nodal members plus the subjects who had the shortest distance to this particular node, taken from the matrix of distances from individuals to syndromes, as outlined in step four of syndrome analysis. It was required that a minimum difference in distance to two nodal points had to be exceeded in order to be included. In other words, subjects who seem to be located approximately halfway between two nodal groups were excluded. The *N* of the extended nodal groups are also entered in Table 35. It was decided to disregard the instances where the extended nodal groups included less than eight individuals, which left the following nodal groups: 1, 2, and 3 in the youngest retarded sample; 1, 2 and 7 in the 12-15 sample; and 1, 2, 3, and 4 in the 20-24 sample. Extended nodal groups could not be formed in the normal sample. The original nodal groups showed much less difference than was the case in the retarded samples, and only one or two normals survived the criterion of the minimum difference in distance to two nodal points.

Group means for the 50 measures of an original and its extended NG were plotted on the same chart, and the difference between them appraised. In most cases there was the closest resemblance between the original and the extended nodal group, in only two or three measures did the difference exceed 7 points. The only exception was NG 2 in the 20-24 sample. This was understandable, in view of the great increase in *N* from the original to the extended group.

A graphic presentation of the group means for the ten extended nodal groups from the retardate samples and the four original nodal groups from the normal sample is shown in Fig. 8.

A problem encountered in determining the essential characteristics of the nodal groups was that the presence of many variables made it very difficult to apprehend by visual inspection the peculiarities of the group. This was particularly the case when all nodal groups in a sample would tend to have high scores or low scores in comparison with the normals, as extreme scores were the best land-marks to use in describing the nodal group characteristics. To facilitate the comparison of nodal groups, all measures were eliminated from a sample if they did not appear to discriminate between the nodal groups within the sample. As criterion for discrimination, a minimum difference of 15 units between the highest and the lowest nodal mean was adopted. This left 27 variables in the youngest retarded sample, 21 in the 12-15 sample, and 29 in the oldest sample. Of these variables, 14 were common for all three samples and these 14 variables constituted the discriminating variables. By adopting a criterion for discriminating variables which demanded occurrence in all three retarded samples, one might possibly overlook developmental trends, but this simplification seemed justified at this preliminary stage. Thus all retarded samples were evaluated by their performance on the following variables: Audiometry L, Audiometry R, Ataxiometry M, Lower Arm, Tapping, Visual RT, Auditory RT, Auditory Choice RT, Scrambled RT, Pegboard R, Pegboard L, Pegboard Both, Railwalking, and Word Association. This list included primarily motor measures.

The variables which discriminated the normal groups were determined by using the same criterion. The discriminating variables were found to be the following 18: Hand Dominance, Eye Dominance, Color Vision, Audiometry L, Audiometry R, Kinesthesis L, Kinesthesis R, Ataxiometry M, Tapping, Auditory RT, Auditory Choice RT, Pegboard R, Pegboard Both, Mirror Drawing Total Time,

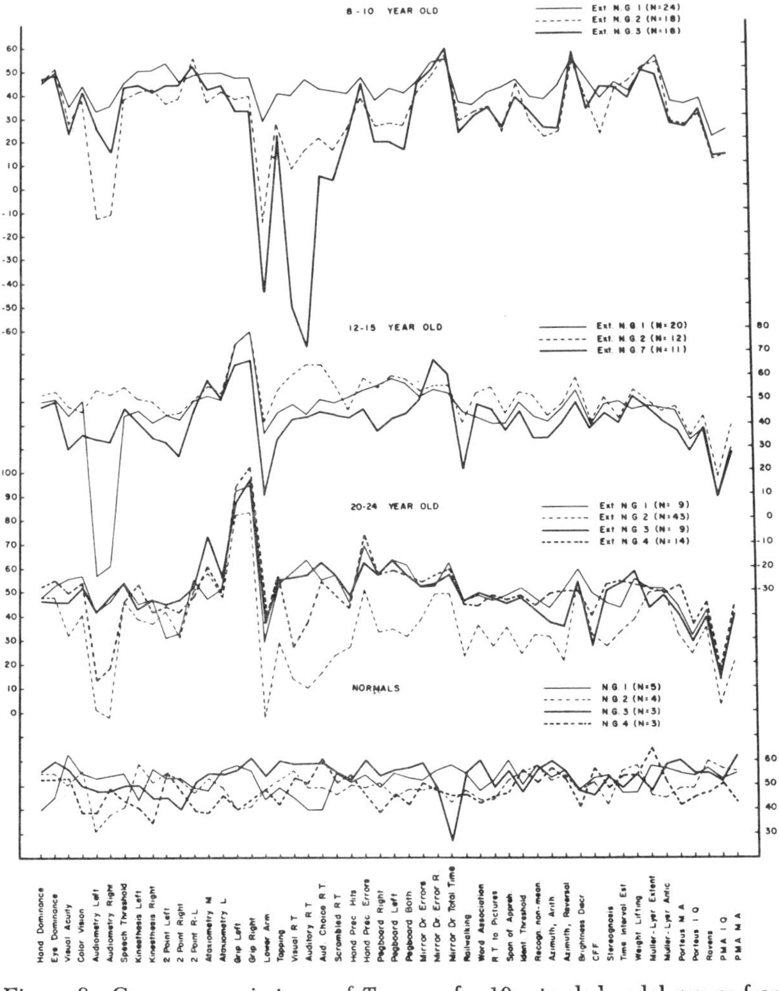

Figure 8. Group means, in terms of T scores, for 10 extended nodal groups from the retarded samples and the four original nodal groups from the normal sample.

Word Association, Muller-Lyer Extent, Porteus MA, and PMA-MA. Only 9 of these 18 were among the 22 variables used for the retardates. Thus there appeared to be some difference as to the measures which discriminate among nodal groups in the retarded and in the normal samples. Among the variables which seemed to have more general discriminatory power were audiometry, simple motor, and verbal speed measures.

Whenever possible, without doing violence to the data, interpretations have been favored which emphasize the similarity between nodal groups. The primary concern, in other words, has been with the broad generalities. In addition to mean for the various measures, the group mean for Mean *T* score and *T* score *SD* have been considered. These means plus PMA-IQ and PMA-MA for the nodal groups are included in Table 35.

The limitations of these descriptions should be clearly understood. In the first place, most of the 14 nodal groups discussed below had questionable statistical foundation because of the small number of subjects in the original nodal groups. Nevertheless, it was believed that the descriptions had some value because some general trends seemed to emerge, in spite of the difficulties involved in sorting a retarded population into orderly groups. A further reason was that these findings might generate more specific hypotheses with regard to grouping of retarded individuals, which in turn might be subject to verification. In the following descriptions, the subscripts refer to sample number.

NG 1_1 had as its most characteristic trend a high general level and a low variability as may be seen from Fig. 8. There was no particular domain of variables which deviated from the normals, and the increase in score with increased complexity of motor tasks was not particularly conspicuous. The original and extended NGs were very similar. The group seemed to be characterized by relatively intact cutaneous and kinesthetic functions, care in the execution of movements at the expense of speed, relatively good perceptual speed and time judgement, and less than normal susceptibility to weight-size illusion. The weaker points appeared to be pure tone threshold, motor and verbal speed, gross motor coordination, and intersensory integration. Since there was but moderate deviation from normals, it appeared to be a General Ability group with an overall slightly subnormal level.

NG 2_1 had considerably lower general performance level. This group consisted of subjects with greater across-trait variability, which was reflected in a more irregular profile for the group. There appeared to be specific deficiency in sensory and intersensory integration and in most of the simple motor tasks. The increase in performance with increase in complexity of motor tasks was marked. While the generally low performance level was noted, the outstanding characteristics of the group were the extreme deviation for pure tone thresholds and low score for Lower Arm Movement.

NG 3_1 represented the extreme in terms of poor performance level and across-trait variability. This group attained highest level in cutaneous discrimination, postural stability, and care in executing motor tasks, while the dramatic deficiency in most of the simpler motor tasks (speed and reactive speed) was the outstanding characteristic. The general course of the curve through the motor measures was similar in shape to that of NG 2_1, but its shape was extreme. Both of these two NGs had a considerably higher score for Tapping than for other simple motor tasks. It is possible that the low audiometric scores should have been regarded as an added characteristic of NG 3_1. If so, there was a certain similarity to NG 2_1, only that the emphasis was shifted from audiometry in NG 2_1 to motor in NG 3_1.

NG 1_2 in Fig. 8 showed an intermediate overall level and included subjects with a rather large across-trait variability. In spite of this, the profile of the group was rather smooth, with the notable exception of the audiometric scores. The curve through the motor scores had a gentle slope. While the low Audiometric Threshold was the outstanding characteristic, it is possible that the simple motor tasks, such as Lower Arm, Tapping, and Audiometry RT, should have been considered as additional characteristics, since it has been noted before that such motor measures change with increasing age, and that these motor scores would have appeared low had they been compared to 12-15 year old normals. Thus the group may be regarded as equivalent to NG 2_1, even if the present group probably had more auditory than motor deficit.

NG 2_2 had the highest overall mean and lowest *T* score *SD* of all NGs in this sample. The overall profile was not as smooth as it was in the previous NG, but it did not have any great deviation. Considering the lack of substantial deviation, and allowing for age increment in the motor scores, the group could possibly have corresponded to NG 1_1 in the youngest sample and may be regarded as a General Ability group, which may also have shown slight subnormality had it been compared to 12-15 age norms.

NG 7_2 had a rather low overall level but while the *T* score *SD* was between that of the other two NGs, the profile was rather jagged. When age development of motor factors was considered, the particular deficiency of the group was probably best reflected by the simple motor functions and Railwalking. The contrast between Tapping and RT measures found in some of the NGs in the youngest sample did not appear here. The deficiency of this group in several sensory and perceptual tasks should not be disregarded, since by this deficiency the group became the first to be characterized by other measures than pure tone threshold and simple motor tasks. In spite of these additional characteristics, it was probably most similar to NG 3_1 but failed to have quite as dramatic deficiencies in some of the RT measures. Thus it emerged as a group handicapped in pure tone, simple motor tasks, gross bodily movement, as well as appraisal and integration of spatial relations.

NG 1_3 had high mean *T* score and relatively low *T* score *SD*, but since this was also true for NGs 3_3 and 4_3 it was not a distinctive feature of the group as it had been in NG 1_1 and NG 2_2. The strong point of the group seemed to be reactive speed and finger dexterity, whereas the deficiencies were for cutaneous space perception and simple motor speed (Lower Arm). While this afforded a certain similarity to the General Ability groups of the other samples, and while age development of motor function tended to obscure the impairment of the simple motor speed measures, the cutaneous space perception and lower arm deficiencies set it apart from the other General NGs.

NG 2_3 was a group with low overall performance level and high across-trait variability. A peculiar situation arose from the fact that the extended group had 14 times as many subjects as the original group, resulting in differences in means but not in distinct changes of general pattern. The group was characterized by generally low level and particular deficiency of auditory and simple motor measures, with Tapping considerably higher than its two neighboring motor measures. Thus it showed considerable resemblance to NG 3_1 and NG 7_2.

NG 3_3 had about the same general level and across-trait variability as NG 1_3. While there was some doubt about what separated NGs 1_3 and 3_3, the fewer low scores in the present group justified the selection of this group as the equivalent to NG 1_1 and NG 2_2—the General Ability groups.

NG 4_3 had about the same general level as NGs 1_3 and 3_3 but somewhat lower mean *T* score *SD*. The group did have the pattern of relatively high Tapping scores in contrast to Lower Arm and Visual RT. The most conspicuous characteristic of the group was the low audiometer scores, supplemented by low scores for simple motor movements. With the emphasis on audiometric deficiency it appeared that this group might correspond to NG 2_1 and NG 1_2.

As has been mentioned, extended nodal groups could not be obtained among the normals, because of the small difference between the original nodal groups. A basic difference between the normals and the retardates was the greater variability of performance among the retardates. A technique, like syndrome analysis, which primarily takes level into consideration, has therefore more power of discrimination among the retardates.

Data for the evaluation of the four nodal groups in the normal sample were therefore limited to the original nodal groups. Table 35 indicates that these groups showed less difference in overall level than did any of the retarded samples. The *T* score *SD* was low and remarkably uniform for the four groups.

The small *N* of the subgroups in the normal sample made them suspect to chance occurrence, as well as of little functional use. For this reason, instead of a complete description, only a few similarities are pointed out.

NG 1_4 was possibly similar to the General Ability group of the retardates.

NG 2_4 may also have been compared to NGs 2_1, 1_2, and 4_3, except that there was no discrepancy between the thresholds for pure tone and speech. It therefore seemed to reflect more general auditory deficiency. The two remaining NGs of the normals appeared to have the characteristics of General Ability groups of somewhat high and low levels.

Thus it appeared that some nodal groups could be distinguished and described better among retardates than among normals. The characteristics which were most frequently discriminating were general level, across-trait variabiliyt, pure tone threshold, simple motor tasks, and, sometimes, cutaneous and visual appraisal of spatial relations. On this basis it seemed possible to identify three NGs with certain similarities within the three retarded samples: Type One, a relatively high level group with little variability and no specific deviations either in positive or negative direction (General Ability Group, NG 1_1, NG 2_2, and NG 3_3); Type Two, an NG with particular impairment in pure tone threshold and with more or less additional impairment of simple motor functions (Auditory-Motor Group, NG 2_1, NG 1_2, and NG 4_3); and Type Three, an NG with particular impairment of simple motor measures which might extend to complex motor measures and perceptual ones, and with regular impairment of pure tone threshold (Motor Auditory Group, NG 3_1, NG 7_2, and NG 2_3). There was only moderate similarity between NGs in retardates and in normals.

It must be admitted as a limitation of the study that control groups were not available for all three age levels of the retardates. The projection of the older retardates against a younger control group is not without hazards. Additional reference samples should be obtained in the future. It is of interest to compare the tentatively described subgroups of retardates in terms of clinical categories of etiology, and of neurological and EEG impairment. Since a small number of subjects had to be distributed over as many as six categories, the distribution of the subjects in the nodal groups over the categories of etiology, and of neurological and EEG impairment was not particularly informative. Instead, the three "types" of retardates indicated by the syndrome analysis were combined across age samples. The precentage distribution over etiological categories and over categories according to degree of EEG and neurological impairment is shown in Table 36.

TABLE 36

DISTRIBUTION (IN PER CENT) OVER ETIOLOGICAL, EEG, AND NEUROLOGICAL CATEGORIES WHEN THE THREE SYNDROME GROUPS ARE COMBINED ACROSS AGE SAMPLES

Fam.	*Org.*	*Unkn.*	*Mix.*	*Mong.*	*N.C.*	*N*	
9%	44	18	22	—	7	(45)	Type One: General
29%	31	10	19	2	10	(52)	Type Two: PT-Motor
4%	51	8	19	10	7	(72)	Type Three: Motor-PT
	EEG				NEURO		
0	1	2	3	0	1	2	Code
34	30	5	32	88	10	2	Type One: General
36	34	6	24	73	24	4	Type Two: PT-Motor
26	30	8	36	46	30	24	Type Three: Motor-PT

It appears from the table that there was not much difference between Type One and Type Three with regard to etiology and EEG. Type Three had a tendency toward slightly heavier representation in the organic category and toward having fewer subjects with normal EEG than had the other two types. Type Two differed from the other two groups by having more familials and somewhat less indication of a clearly abnormal EEG pattern. With respect to neurological signs there was less difference between Type One and Type Two, while Type Three distinguished itself by having more subjects in the category of severe neurological impairment. Thus it appeared that Type One, characterized by general ability, was predominantly of organic etiology, had relatively many subjects with EEG abnormality but very few with positive neurological signs. Type Two, with emphasis on pure tone deficiency, seemed to include most of the familials, had the least EEG abnormality and few subjects with positive neurological signs. Type Three, with emphasis on deficiency of simple motor tasks, was predominantly of organic etiology. It had relatively many subjects with EEG abnormality and relatively many with positive neurological signs. Thus the three types which were indicated by the syndrome analysis suggested different patterns of etiology, and of EEG and neurological impairment when the groups were combined, even though neither of the clinical classifications alone was able to clearly discriminate the types.

Both inverse factor analysis and syndrome analysis have indicated subgroups of our subject samples. The question arises how the subgroups resulting from the two procedures are related. Both procedures show agreement in that a relatively large number of subjects had a tendency to fall into a General Ability group, while there were relatively few subjects in the remaining groups, except for the 43 subjects in the Extended NG 2 in the oldest retarded sample. Because of the small *N* in the remaining groups, the description of their characteristics must be regarded as tentative.

On the basis of the correlations between factor loading and variables, it did not appear that Types Two and Three from the syndrome analysis were identified by the inverse factor analysis. Nowhere was the particular relationship of pure tone threshold and simple motor task to the factor loadings conspicuous. When, however, one consulted the graphs where the group means for positive and negative factor loadings were plotted separately, it was possible to find groups which exhibited the mentioned constellations. Tabulating the number of individuals common in Subject Factors and Nodal Group Types, the results of Table 37 were obtained.

Thus in the 8-10 retarded sample, Negative SF 1_1 seemed to correspond to NG 1_1, in that both included a number of common individuals who performed on a generally high level with low across-trait

TABLE 37

NUMBER OF SUBJECTS WHICH OCCUR IN BOTH SF GROUPS AND NODAL GROUPS (LIMITED TO CASES WHERE AT LEAST A MODERATE OVERLAP EXISTS)

	1 *N in SF*	*2* *N in orig. NG*	*3* *N in ext. NG*	*4* *2 in 1*	*5* *3 in 1*
8–10					
Neg. SF 1_1 – NG 1_1	19	17	24	13	17
Pos. SF 1_1 – NG 3_1	22	5	18	4	14
Neg. SF 4_1 – NG 2_1	5	5	18	0	3
12–15					
Pos. SF 1_2 – NG 2_2	29	4	12	2	7
Neg. SF 2_2 – NG 1_2	8	8	20	5	7
20–24					
Pos. SF 1_3 – NG 4_3	13	3	14	2	6
Neg. SF 1_3 – NG 2_3	6	3	43	0	6

variability—the Type One Syndrome. Negative SF 4_1 showed no overlap with Original NG 2_1 but, tentatively considered as a possible audio factor, was largely contained in extended NG 2_1 and therefore included subjects with Type Two Syndrome. Positive SF 1_1 exhibited considerable overlap with NG 3_1, characterized by low scores for simple motor tasks and pure tone threshold, with emphasis on the former—i.e., Type Three Syndrome. Here, there was also agreement with respect to a relatively high Tapping score in contrast to low scores for Lower Arm and Visual RT.

In the 12-15 sample there was correspondence between positive SF 1_2 and NG 2_2 in identifying subjects with Type One Syndrome. In this case, NG 2_2 seemed to be contained within SF 1_2 with about two-thirds of the Extended NG subjects in common. Negative SF 2_2, also treated as a tentative audio factor, corresponded to NG 1_2 with considerable overlap of subjects with Type Two Syndrome. There seemed to be no SF corresponding to Type Three Syndrome in this sample.

In the 20-24 sample Type One Syndrome had no SF counterpart in terms of overlapping subjects. Positive SF 1_3 corresponded to NG 4_3 (Type Two Syndrome) in that most of the original NG subjects and almost one-half of the extended NG subjects were contained within it. Negative SF 1_3 was contained within NG 2_3 (Type Three Syndrome) although the *N*s were so widely different that they were probably tapping different subject characteristics.

In the normal sample there seemed to be no correspondence between SFs for the inverse factor analysis and the NGs from the syndrome analysis. The primary reason for this was that syndrome analysis did not discriminate clear subgroups. Among the retardates the most clearly defined subgroups with the largest *N*s were those which showed the best correspondence between the two techniques. The fact that correspondence was found among these subgroups argues against their chance occurrence and lends weight to their validity.

If subgroups of retardates are to have any significance for research, training, and treatment, one must be able to determine directly from his test scores the subgroup to which an individual belongs. Merely to get a feeling of the problems which will be encountered in this connection, an attempt was made to sort the retarded subjects on the basis of level and pattern of selected variables. Since pure tone thresholds and simple motor tasks seemed to be key variables in two of the suggested subgroups, this survey was limited to Auditory L, Lower Arm, and Simple Auditory RT. The following categories emerged clearly from the level and pattern of the three variables:

Generally High, Intermediate, Generally Low, Auditory High-Motor Low, Auditory Low-Motor High, Lower Arm less than RT, and Miscellaneous. As a check on the reliability of this sorting, the sorting was repeated in all three retarded samples and about 80% of the subjects were assigned to the same category as in the first sorting. Next, relationship between these sorted groups and nodal groups was established. For the three retarded samples combined, it was found that of the individuals included in Type One Syndrome, 60% were classified as Generally High Performance on the basis of three scores. Subjects in Type Two Syndrome (Auditory low) were represented with 33% of their membership in the category Motor High-Auditory Low and 17% in Lower Arm less than RT. Of Type Three Syndrome subjects (motor performance low), 40% were found in the categories of Generally Low (19%) and Auditory High-Motor Low (21%).

Also, the relationship between the sorted groups and SF groups was surveyed. Only high and low performance from the General Ability Factor were considered, since the other SFs could not be defined with any degree of precision. Here it was found that 79% of the subjects who were defined as high scorers by the inverse factor analysis were distributed over the following three categories: Generally High Level (46%) Motor High-Auditory Low (22%), and Lower Arm Less Than RT (11%). Of the low scorers 71% were in the two categories: Generally Low (42%) and Auditory High-Motor Low (29%).

While the tentative nature of this exploration should be clearly understood, it does suggest that when subgroups of retardates are better defined they may be identified from a relatively small number of key tests.

Discussion

The two statistical procedures which have been used here to fractionate the subject samples differ in very important ways: one is based on correlation between subjects and the other is based on the difference in performance level between subjects. Neither takes into account the particular feature of the other. They also differ in methods of interpretation; one is interpreted on the basis of correlations between factor loading and test score, while the other is interpreted on the basis of those variables which differentiate between nodal groups. Under these circumstances the amount of similarity in the outcome of the two procedures was reassuring. It appears that inverse factor analysis was not a successful method for producing subgroups beyond the General Ability group, primarily because the bipolar factors were splitting the populations into so many groups, with so few individuals in each, that it became hazardous to interpret such groups and made their practical value questionable. The syndrome analysis did not suffer from this limitation, and suggested two additional subgroups. It is a puzzle as to why this procedure, based as it was on distance squared, should yield these two subgroups which had usually poor performance on both pure tone threshold and simple motor tasks, the main difference being on which type of function the emphasis was placed. This may well be an artifact and the possibility that Syndrome Types Two and Three actually belong together should be kept in mind.

Among the normals, the subgroups indicated by inverse factor analysis seemed better defined and seemed to make more sense than those resulting from syndrome analysis. The fact that difference in general level was much smaller among the normals than among the retardates was of considerable importance in this respect. This might therefore have been a situation which favored the inverse factor analysis, whereas the greater differences among the retardates provided a more appropriate situation for syndrome analysis.

A suggested difference in result between the two procedures was that inverse factor analysis assigned far more importance to intellectual and spatial appraisal functions than did the syndrome analysis. The significance of this can only be determined by further research.

It appeared that the normals exhibited different patterns of abilities related to the higher degree of differentiation while the overall performance level varied within a narrow range. Thus a correlational analysis indicated subgroups while a fractionation procedure which was based on distance squared did not seem appropriate for the task. The reversed situation was found for the retardates. Here the differentiation of abilities was impaired and, therefore, correlational procedures were not particularly efficient in differentiating subgroups. On the other hand, overall levels differed substantially in retardates, and therefore a distance squared technique was more adequate. Thus it appeared that the use of different techniques showed the highest degree of efficiency in defining subgroups of normals and retardates.

From Fig. 7 it can be seen that the difference in performance between subjects with positive and negative loadings on the General Ability Factor was particularly great for the simple motor tasks, those reflecting response initiation and effort. Also these subjects tended to have low Pure Tone Threshold. The similarity here to the main characteristics of the Syndrome Types may indicate that in the retardates we are primarily dealing with degree of retardation, and as the performance level decreases the impairment is most clearly reflected in the pure tone threshold and the simple motor tasks. In other words, Pure Tone Threshold, Lower Arm Movement, and RT may be the most sensitive indicators of general ability level. Discussion in earlier sections pointed out that low performance on these tasks may be interpreted as impairment of arousal, vigilance, and effort rather than impairment of learning or specific motor functions. It may be well to repeat that these interpretations are not to be generalized to include retardates which fall outside the samples of this study. Undoubtedly there are retardates with specific disabilities.

At the present stage of knowledge it seems more appropriate to regard inverse factor analysis and syndrome analysis as supplementary procedures rather than as competitors. The attempt to define subgroups of retardates is only in its initial stage. We need more information as to the battery of tests which is the most adequate for the purpose, and we need improved statistical techniques for the fractionation of a sample into homogeneous subgroups. While it is likely that considerable time will pass before this information is available, we think that the results of the present investigation are sufficiently encouraging to proceed with some vigor. The logical next step is to repeat the present study with the reduced battery discussed earlier, supplemented by techniques of analysis which adequately provide for both level and pattern.

Summary

From the Nodal Groups indicated by the syndrome analysis, Extended Nodal Groups were formed, i.e., the original NGs were extended to include individuals who had the closest distance to a particular nodal point. Extended NGs which included more than eight were selected for further considerations. The characteristics of these groups were determined on the basis of 14 variables which differed by more than 15 units between extreme nodal means in all retarded samples.

It was found that three Syndromes appeared in all retarded samples: Type One, a relatively high level group with little variability and no specific deviation either in positive or negative direction; Type Two, a group with particular impairment in pure tone threshold, with more or less additional impairment of simple motor functions; and Type Three, a group with particular impairment of simple motor measures which may extend to complex motor measures and perceptual ones, and with regular impairment of pure tone threshold.

In the normal sample, the nodal points were too close together to differentiate subgroups, thus it seems that different statistical methods are most effective in defining subgroups in retardates and normals.

There was a reasonable overlap between the General Ability groups as they were defined by inverse factor analysis and syndrome analysis. A preliminary attempt to identify the subjects in the three syndrome groups by means of three variables was sufficiently promising to invite further investigation.

The findings have been interpreted to indicate that variation in general performance level is particularly important in retardates and that pure tone threshold and simple motor tasks are particularly sensitive indicators of the general level. The involvement of these variables suggests that impairment of general factors such as arousal, vigilance, and effort, more than impairment of specific functions, is characteristic of the retardates.

V RESUME AND DISCUSSION

SAMPLE COMPARISONS

The present study has shown that measures of the type included in the ASP battery can be recorded with a high degree of reliability in retarded subjects. It has been found that there is very little difference in performance between the two sexes for either retardates or normals. Only four variables—Grip, Mirror Drawing Total Time, Azimuth, and CFF—showed better scores for boys than for girls in all four samples, with two or more of them significant. On this basis the boys and the girls were pooled.

When the test scores of the retardates were converted to standard scores (*T* scores) in terms of Mean and *SD* of the normals, the profiles which emerged from the three retarded samples had considerable similarity, even if differences were also evident. This similarity prevailed even though the retardates had a considerably larger variability than had the normals for the great majority of the measures. The multivariate analysis has indicated that some subgroups of the samples contribute more heavily to the characteristic landmarks than do others. The large General Ability subgroup, however, also indicated a trend toward similarity which introduces a concept of a general structure of abilities in retardates.

For very few variables did any of the retarded samples exceed the level of the normal 8-10 year old sample. Apparently there is more justification for regarding these subjects as permanently deficient rather than retarded, if the latter term is used in the sense of delayed development. While there probably are individuals who are properly described by the term retarded, these individuals may be found more often in the public schools and special classes than in institutions such as those from which the present populations have been drawn.

For the sensory measures, all the retarded samples generally had group means within 1 *SD* below the normal sample. The outstanding exception was the low score for the two pure tone thresholds coexisting with a near to normal speech threshold. The interpretation has been that while sensory impairment is probably more frequent among the retardates, it is of greater importance that the retardates fail when the testing procedure places severe demand on sustained attention. The prime example of this is the pure tone thresholds.

The degree to which the variables are affected by age differs according to task domain. The sensory tasks showed no improvement with age. The only indication to the contrary was in visual acuity and color vision, which has been interpreted in terms of insufficient directional concepts and reading ability as well as of testing procedure.

The motor variables had the most conspicuous growth pattern of all variables. Strength of grip stands out as the measure where performance is most closely related to development until adult age. This variable seems to be related to Ataxiometry and there are conflicting indications as to its relationship to Stereognosis. The literature indicates that development of motor tasks has not reached maximum level at the age of 8-10 in the normals. On this basis it appears that the retardates are impaired with respect to motor performance, particularly simple motor tasks, even though they show some improvement with age. It is evident then, that deficiency, rather than retardation of development, best describes this segment of the population.

The difference between age groups was considerably less for perceptual measures where scores had a clear tendency to remain below the normal level even for the older retardates. Thus perceptual measures appear to reach maturity at an earlier age than do motor measures, and do not possess as much power of discrimination. This difference between motor and perceptual measures is borne out by the result of traditional factor analysis.

Since the three retarded samples were selected on the basis of IQ, little can be said about developmental trends for the complex mental measures.

It has been found that the retarded samples differ from the normals in characteristic ways, and that they differ from each other in a manner which is related to development and maturation in various functions, supporting the concept of a retardate structure of abilities.

Not all differences between the retarded samples can be accounted for by difference in age, since scores of the oldest retarded sample generally are found between those of the youngest and the 12-15 sample. A similar tendency was noted in the analysis of test correlations. Since the oldest sample was drawn from institutions having very active programs, the assumption would seem to be refuted that the oldest retardates have regressed because of lack of stimulating living conditions. Thus the "regression" has been related to the sampling problem.

The dominating finding of the motor measures is that complex motor tasks are relatively better performed than are simple motor tasks. This relationship, however, seems to be limited to manipulative and speed tasks. As in the case of the pure tone threshold, this has been attributed to the special demand made for alertness and effort in performing simple motor tasks.

Since these motor tasks are so simple to perform, the motivational or drive factors have been given particular consideration. Of interest here is the fact that the repetitive act of tapping was better performed than were the speed measures of Lower Arm and RTs. Thus, rather than the response itself, initiation of the response is implicated, especially when left to the subject. In a recent study, King (1965) compared the performance of normal and psychotic subjects on four measures: time to initiate response, time to initiate and to complete a thrust response, time of traverse to cue given by experimenter, and time of traverse at own volition. For all measures he found significantly longer responses for the psychotic group. Of considerable interest is that in the normals, traverse cued by the subject himself was significantly slower than if the same traverse was cued by the experimenter. In the psychotic group the self-cued traverse was longer than the others, even if the difference did not reach significant proportions. This indicates that self-initiated effort is impaired in other abnormal populations as well. Among the motor measures, Railwalking appeared to be considerably impaired in all three retarded samples and was one of the few variables discriminating neurological and EEG subgroups. It has been discussed in terms of failure of integration of larger muscle groups. Also considered has been the possibility that it is not the coordinating activity of the muscles themselves which is affected but the simultaneous handling of kinesthetic and visual cues. A third possibility is a differential impairment of dynamic rather than static equilibrium (Ataxiometry). Only with further research can less alternatives be evaluated.

The perceptual measures were generally well below the normal level; more than half were significantly so. While not consistent, there was a trend for the more complex perceptual tasks (coordination of cues) to be not significantly different from the normals. Conversely, the simpler perceptual measures tended to be significantly different. Thus the relationship observed for the motor tasks between task complexity and performance level may also hold true for the perceptual tasks.

The complex mental functions were all well below normal level, more so for the age related IQ than for the MA measure. The retardates also appeared to have more difficulties with the academically oriented and more composite PMA than with the Porteus and the Raven where spatial relations are more important. It was also interesting to observe that the complex mental functions seemed to be relatively more impaired in the two older than in the youngest retarded sample. This pattern is probably a result of sampling procedure. As has been discussed previously, those in the youngest sample had the highest rejection rate because many of them were not able to perform the required tasks. It is also quite probable that the cases which remain in an institution after maturity are biased in the other direction. Even in the developmental sample where the three age groups were equated for IQ, the oldest sample occupied a position between the other two samples. If sampling bias is the pertinent factor, it would seem to suggest that overall lack of abilities, rather than IQ itself, prevents these 20-24 year olds from being discharged from their institutions. The best way of settling this problem would be to retest some of the 12-15 year olds when they reach their 20th year.

From the general level of the intellectual tasks and from the relation found for the various intellectual measures it has been concluded that the integrative mechanism of complex mental functioning is a primary manifestation of retardation, and that the composite intelligence measures remain among the most significant diagnostic procedures for the retarded segment of the population.

The overall analysis of variance showed no discrimination between normal and retarded samples for the following six variables: Eye Dominance, Two-Point Difference, Brightness Discrimination, Mirror Drawing Error Range, Muller-Lyer Extent, and Anticipation. While Identification did not reach this criterion for *F*, it showed no significant sample differences by a somewhat stricter criterion. Some of these variables may justify additional comments. The fact that Two-Point Difference was not a discriminating variable seems to indicate the lack of localized cortical lesions and to suggest that the level of Two-Point Thesholds in the retardates may be a result of attention or motivation factors. The mean Identification Threshold was above those of the retardates but the differences did not reach significance level because of the variability in the retarded samples. Brightness Discrimination presented a puzzling finding indeed. While the exact reason is not obvious, the procedure for recording the difference limen may have been at fault. In another study (Clausen and Karrer, 1963) where the same technique was used for normal adult subjects, a test-retest reliability coefficient of .31 was found. It was suggested that the low reliability resulted from a failure to standardize the dark adaptation of the subjects. While this criticism may apply to the present study, split-half reliability was high, and the consistency in the three retarded samples lends weight to the finding.

Measures of individual variability (generally expressed by range) were originally included in the study. As it became necessary to reduce the number of variables, it was found that these variability measures were highly correlated with the individual central tendency measures. On this basis they were excluded except for Mirror Drawing Error Range, which did not discriminate between the four samples. The Mirror Drawing and Hand Precision tasks had both a speed score and an error score which have a reciprocal relation. There are indications in the data that these two cannot be classified simply as motor tasks. The thought has been entertained that they may be regarded as indices of motivation, but even in this respect they were not consistent. In the final analysis both are recommended for exclusion. This recommendation has been made with some hesitation, because these tests showed without question relatively high performance level of the retardates. While it may be assumed that the high level for Mirror Drawing resulted from less well-established eye-hand coordination and therefore less interference when the star pattern was viewed in the mirror; a similar explanation does not exist for Hand Precision. Ratio between Hand Precision Hits and Errors has been interpreted to indicate task attitude—caution in making errors—while motor coordination is indicated by general level of performance. It may be that the task arouses more interest while at the same time requiring no particular degree of determination, and, like Tapping, initiation of response may be of relatively little importance. Again, it appears that more complex motor tasks are better performed than simpler motor tasks.

In view of Jenkin's (1959) findings of significant differences in amount of illusion between the organic retardates and normals, the present findings were unexpected. While Muller-Lyer and Weight Lifting both showed less illusion in the retardates than in the normals, supporting Jenkin's findings, ASP data showed significance only between the youngest retardates and the normals for Weight Lifting.

In comparison to the normals, the youngest retarded sample had significantly lower scores for 39 of the 50 variables. The 11 non-significant variables were distributed between sensory and perceptual tasks. The 12-15 sample was also significantly lower for 24 variables. Most of these 24 variables were included in the 39 above. Of the remaining 15 variables, 12 were in the domain of motor functions.

Since motor functions have not matured in normals at 8-10, it is suggested that the 12-15 retardates should have much the same relationship to 12-15 normals as 8-10 retardates have to normals of their age. It has been concluded that all three retarded samples are less motivated and have less demand for quality performance than have the normal sample. The latter, while younger, had a higher MA and their general superiority over retardates may have been related to this. A similar picture emerged from the comparison of the oldest retarded with the normals. For Stereognosis and four of the motor measures significant differences which had disappeared in the 12-15 sample were here restored by a regression in performance level.

The essential outcome of the comparison of the three retarded samples may be summarized thus: the domains of sensory and complex functions showed similarity in level as well as in patterns. The domain of motor functions showed general similarity in patterns but pronounced differences in level. The domain of perceptual functions showed relatively small differences in level and less consistency in patterns than did the functions of the other domains. Since there seemed to be emphasis on level rather than on pattern, and since there were clear differences between performances of retardates and normals, the concept of a retarded ability structure received support. In this structure there are some variables which better reflect retardation than do others. These variables and the functions they are assumed to measure in the present study are as follows: Audiometry—attention, motivation or alertness; Lower Arm Movement—response initiation and effort or drive; RT measures—alertness, fine motor coordination, and effort; and Railwalking—integration of gross motor movements and visual cues. In the complex mental functions and several perceptual tasks the critical function seems to be integration. Measures like Mirror-Drawing, Weight Lifting, and Muller-Lyer may be adequately performed by the retardates because their more limited experience with the outside world has not established sufficiently firm patterns to interfere with the performance of these tasks, as is the case with the normals.

The developmental sample served for further comparison between the three retarded samples. The youngest developmental sample differed from the two older ones in 22 variables which were fairly equally distributed over all categories. The perceptual tasks which differed seem to require more judgement and to be more complex. Five measures, four being from the motor domain, differed from the 12-15 sample but not from the 20-24 sample, due to regression of performance by the latter. Thus it appeared that between the ages 8-10 and 12-15 there was extensive development in the retardates. This development did not seem to have continued into adult age, and may even have been reversed at that stage; as was indicated by the trend of the oldest retarded sample toward lower scores as compared with the 12-15 sample.

Throughout the study it has been emphasized that simple motor tasks in retardates seem relatively more impaired than do complex motor tasks, and this has been interpreted in terms of lack of drive, sustained attention, or effort. Although not as clear, the same trend was indicated for perceptual measures. It seems, however, that if developmental trends are considered, the perceptual tasks were relatively better performed than were the simple motor tasks. This is another puzzling finding. It is contrary to what might have been expected on the basis of attention and cognitive integrative factors which would seem to be necessary for the performance of the perceptual tasks. This dilemma can only be solved by determining the reasons for the surprisingly poor performance by the retardates on the simple motor tasks.

As a result of different development rates for the various measures, five different developmental trends have been listed: (a.) continued development up to adult age (muscular strength, static equilibrium, and weight-size illusion); (b.) development to age 12-15 followed by a decline (motor speed and manipulation, dynamic equilibrium, and some complex perceptual measures); (c.) gradual decline with age (kinesthesis and cutaneous space discrimination); (d.) no development but different from normals (pure tone threshold and perceptual variables requiring simple judgement of qualitative relations); and (e.) no development and not different from normals (laterality and some perceptual measures requiring judgement of quantitative relations).

The group means for the Mean *T* score corroborate many of the points made above. The primary new contribution is the suggestion that the reversals in the oldest retarded sample are more characteristic for the boys than for the girls.

The *T* score *SD* indicated that in addition to the greater variability within the retarded sample there was also greater individual across-trait variability. Thus prediction of general ability level from a limited number of variables is more hazardous in retardates than in normals. Mean *T* score and *T* score *SD* were both correlated to IQ, the former directly and the latter inversely. The rather high correlation between Mean *T* score and PMA-IQ shows that this intelligence test is an estimate of general ability.

When the ASP findings are compared with previous reports, there is general agreement with regard to overall level for the various measures in both retardates and normals and with regard to sex difference. The literature also revealed that motor variables develop beyond 8-10 age level in retardates, indicating that the two older samples for these variables were as much behind their age norm as were the youngest retardates.

The main discrepancy is that previous investigators have found a direct relationship between performance level and task complexity for motor variables, in contrast to the present finding.

The data have shown that subdivision of the retarded population according to neurological signs, EEG abnormality and both combined is not particularly productive. Only comparisons between extreme groups—but not adjacent groups—have shown significant differences. It seems indicated that neurological examination and/or EEG pattern have greater discriminatory power than etiological classification. Also it appears that manual strength, finger coordination (Pegboard), and gross body movement (Railwalking) are the tasks which are most sensitive to such indices of cortical impairment. With abnormal EEG there has also been a tendency to impairment of interpretation of abstract concepts, such as span of apprehension, sustained attention, foresight and planning, and task attitude. In the samples of the present study there seemed to be no relation between level (Mean *T* score) or across-trait variability and signs of CNS impairment.

The comparison of etiological categories was negative. Thus our results did not show the same distinct differences between familial and organic etiologies as has been shown by other investigators (e.g., Werner and Thuma, 1942 a and b; Werner and Strauss, 1940, 1941; and Strauss and Werner, 1941, 1942 a and b). One apparent reason for this may be that our subjects were not selected on the basis of etiology, and that our criteria excluded the most distinct organics. The difference between the present and some previous findings with respect to etiology may therefore be due to difference in sample population. While our data may not be directly comparable to those of Werner and Strauss, the discrepancies may be significant. It may be that a sharp contrast between familial and organic subjects does not exist when the organic impairment is less obvious and less localized. It is possible that mild organic impairment is of a similar nature to the functional impairment or incomplete development which occurs in the familial retardates. The consequences of this would be that the etiological distinction into familials and organics, at least of the milder cases, has limited significance, as it does not reflect behavioral differences.

CORRELATION BETWEEN MEASURES

It has been assumed that increase in differentiation and integration is a normal developmental trend which is impaired in the mentally retarded. Level of performance has been regarded as an indicator of integration, and on this basis it appears that rarely do the retarded samples reach the level of integration of normal 8-10 year olds. Thus while this analysis seems to stress impaired differentiation, the importance of impaired integration should not be overlooked. Differentiation or individuation of motor functions in early life was stressed by Coghill (1930). Gesell (1933) defined development as a process of continuous differentiation, and Goodenough (1945, p. 232) stated: "The principle of development by differentiation, first noted in the study of physical growth, has been found to apply to most aspects of mental growth as well." Lindsley (1957) discussed differentiation of brain fields in terms of synchronization as a result of growth, maturation and experience. The concept of differentiation played an important role in Lewin's (1946) theoretical discussion of behavior and development. He stated (p. 796) that the significance of differentiation has been demonstrated for the development of language, knowledge, social interaction, emotions and actions. In an earlier publication, Lewin (1935, p. 187) had observed about the feeble-minded: "From the dynamic point of view, this kind of child is defined as a person who has a less differentiated structure, like that of a younger child." It appears, however, that no systematic attempt has been made to make a detailed investigation of differentiation through correlation analysis, either for normal or retarded children. Thus the present findings cannot readily be compared with previous findings, even if scattered correlations may exist.

Correlations between variables have been regarded as indicators of differentiation in the sense that high correlations reflect lack of differentiation–i.e., highly correlated variables do not reach a high degree of independence. On this basis it was assumed that level of performance would be inversely related to magnitude of correlation coefficients. Negative correlations were found for this relationship for all retarded samples.

The overall correlations in the four correlation matrices were generally low, and in accordance with expectation somewhat lower for normals than for retardates. The selection factor in the oldest and youngest retarded samples possibly enhanced the mean correlation in the former and lowered it in the latter sample. It appeared that differentiation was also moderately well developed in the retarded samples, as the correlations were generally low: eight variables did not reach a correlation of .40 with any of the 49 variables in any of the four samples.

The correlations differed for the several domains of variables; with sensory and perceptual variables reaching the highest level of differentiation, motor measures occuping an intermediate position, and complex mental functions attaining the least degree of differentiation. Differentiation between sensory and motor, as well as sensory and perceptual, measures seemed to be well advanced, while that between motor and perceptual tasks was slightly less so. Complex mental functions seemed to be best differentiated from sensory tasks, less from perceptual, and least from motor tasks. The strong relationship between intellectual and motor functions was a specific characteristic of the retardates, again emphasizing the significance of motor functions in these subjects. In terms of development, it appeared that differentiation levels off earliest for sensory and perceptual measures, somewhat later for motor performance, and last for intellectual functions.

A systematic survey of the correlation matrices has given some clue as to which functions show impaired differentiation in the retardates. On this basis there was no indication of less differentiation for sensory functions. This was probably related to the fact that, with exception of pure tone threshold, no substantial indication of impaired sensory functions was found. For motor functions there seemed to be general lack of differentiation: finger-, hand-, arm-, and gross body coordination lacked differentiation from each other and from strength of grip and motor speed.

Differentiation of motor from perceptual functions was also impaired: motor speed was less differentiated from apprehension span, and gross body movement was less differentiated from quick appraisal of spatial relations as well as from the integration of tactual-kinesthetic cues. To a less extent, hand manipulation was also less differentiated from tactual-visual cues.

Perceptual functions which seemed to be lacking in differentiation from each other were: apprehension span, appraisal of spatial relations, recognition, and integration of tactual-visual information.

Intellectual functions seemed in the retardates to be less differentiated from fine, large, and gross motor coordination, and from strength and motor speed. While the picture differed somewhat at the three age levels, intellectual functions seemed to have impaired differentiation from the perceptual functions of apprehension span, appraisal of spatial relations, recognition, and integration of tactual-visual cues.

Thus lack of differentiation seemed to occur in the retardates with reference to a large number of functions. Since differentiation may be regarded as a prerequisite of integration, the lack of differentiation would give rise to poor performance level (integration) in the retardates. The domains of functions which achieved the highest degree of differentiation—sensory and perceptual variables—were the same as those showing little difference between normals and retardates and those in which maturation is reached relatively early. In contrast, the domains of motor and complex mental function were lacking in differentiation, showed the most conspicious difference in level between retardates and normals, and had the longest developmental period. Thus the relationship between differentiation and integration assumed above was supported. It may also be indicated that the more passive acts—sensory function and the predominantly "passive" integration of perceptual function—are less impaired than the active acts—motor function and the complex mental function—which involve more active integration. This is, however, a mere suggestion which may not stand up under closer scrutiny. There is the further question as to how the process of differentiation becomes impaired. For an explanation one would probably have to turn to neurophysiological theory.

TRADITIONAL FACTOR ANALYSIS

The factors which emerge from the traditional factor analysis are often limited to high factor loadings on a few interdependent measures. Consequently they have been relatively easy to interpret, but there is some question as to whether these loadings may be artificially enhanced because of this interdependence. The present findings may therefore be regarded as preliminary until the study is repeated with a modified battery. The traditional factor analysis has had moderate success with respect to characterizing subgroups resulting from the inverse factor analysis. The potential of the traditional factor analysis in this respect is clearly indicated, however, since the most dominating test factor is found to characterize the best defined subgroup. With respect to reducing the test battery, the traditional factor analysis—in addition to group comparison (analysis of variance) and correlation analysis—has contributed significantly; and a suggestion for reducing the test battery from 33 to 21 tests has been presented.

When the trends which had been found in two or more of the samples have been considered, the following factors have been identified: General Ability, General Intelligence (Intellectual-Perceptual and Spatially Related Intellectual), Visual Acuity, Auditory Acuity, Reactive Motor Speed, Cutaneous Space Discrimination, Kinesthesis, Steadiness, Eye-Hand Coordination, Hand Dominance, and Strength of Grip. The first seven of these factors seemed to occur in all four samples, the following two occurred in three samples, and the last three occurred in two samples only and must be regarded with suspicion. Some of these factors showed a tendency to differentiate with age. Thus the General Intelligence factor was found only in the youngest retarded sample, while in the other samples it appeared to have developed into two separate factors: an Intellectual-Perceptual and a Spatially Related Intellectual factor. Hand Dominance appeared as a factor in the youngest retarded and in the normal but not in the two older retarded samples. Also Auditory Acuity had more of the character of general sensory discrimination in the two 8-10 year samples, but seemed to be a purer auditory factor in the two retarded samples.

In general there seemed to be a certain similarity in the factors of the four samples, since seven common factors appeared. While little difference was found between the three retarded samples, the relative importance of factors seemed to differ in the normals. The main difference was that the extent of generality and amount of variance accounted for by the General Ability factor was greater in the retardates than in the normals. In the retardates there was also more emphasis on the Auditory Acuity factor and less emphasis on the Intellectual and the Spatially Related Intelligence factors than in the normals. There also seemed to be a closer relationship between mental and physical abilities in the retardates, which was probably related to the higher degree of differentiation in the normals. Particularly to be noted was that general ability and strength were much more independent functions in normals than in retardates.

In keeping with observations repeatedly made throughout the study, perceptual measures were never systematically dominant in a factor. As a consequence most of the perceptual tests have disappeared in the reduced battery. It would seem extremely important to bring further evidence to this question as it has serious implications for the characteristics which may most profitably be investigated in mental retardation.

SUBGROUPS OF RETARDATES

With respect to our attempts to define subgroups of the mentally retarded, inverse factor analysis and syndrome analysis both indicated the existence of a General Ability Group, characterized chiefly by high performance level and by low across-trait variability. The General Ability Subject factor was bipolar, with one pole corresponding to the First Syndrome Type. This subgroup indicated a generalized rather than specific impairment.

In addition to the General Ability Group, the syndrome analysis has suggested two other subgroups of retardates, one chiefly characterized by impairment of simple motor tasks and additional impairment of pure tone threshold, and the other by deficiency of pure tone threshold with or without concomitant impairment of simple motor tasks. Thus those syndromes differed from each other primarily by relative emphases on pure tone threshold and on simple motor tasks.

The oldest retardates seemed to be more easily subdivided than the youngest. This may have been due to developmental factors or to the differences of the samples created by the selection procedure.

Again, it is not easy to see how a fractionating procedure which is based on distance squared could have distinguished these two groups. Their separate existence, however, was supported by differences noted with respect to etiological classification, neurological impairment and EEG abnormality. From the sorting of the retarded individuals on the basis of level and pattern of three variables, it was found that different patterns characterized these subgroups. It may also have been that these subgroups differed with respect to differentiation, a possibility which should be kept in mind in future research.

It seems to be generally accepted that various etiological subgroups of retardates have characteristic constellations of abilities. The present finding from the inverse factor analysis indicates that the normals fall into more easily distinguishable groups than do the retardates. On the other hand, the retardates can more easily be subdivided by syndrome analysis than can the normals. That the two techniques for fractionating are differentially effective for the normals and retardates seems to support the notion of a general "retardate ability structure" with more difference in level than in pattern. Specific measures—Pure Tone Threshold, Lower Arm Movement, and RT—seem to be particularly sensitive indicators of low performance level. Thus there is general agreement between the interpretation of the ability profiles, the comparison between the etiological samples, the correlation analysis, the traditional factor analysis, and the attempts at defining subgroups of retardates.

From the ASP findings a general picture emerged of the retardates included in the study. The retardates showed some characteristic differences from the normals with respect to performance level of the various measures. While the retarded samples had smaller *SD* than the normals had for the complex mental functions, they had considerably higher *SD* for practically all the other tasks. They also had higher across-trait variabilities than had the normals, and for some variables—particularly sensory and perceptual ones—there was a high degree of independence. These indications of greater differences in the retardates were opposed by the finding of less differentiation than in the normals—particularly for motor and complex mental functions; by the greater dominance of the General factor in the traditional factor analysis; by a single subject group in the inverse factor analysis; and by the three syndrome groups which seemed related to generally high and generally low performance level. These apparently opposing trends may be reconciled by assuming that the retardates were actually not more homogeneous than the normals; but that they differed from each other in so many little ways which prevented the formation of identifiable subgroups. The normals were more homogeneous, they showed less difference in over-all level, but in spite of this they had more identifiable subgroups as determined by inverse factor analysis. In differentiation, the emphasis was on pattern in the normals but on level in the retardates. Related to the lower performance level in the retardates was the lack of differentiation of functions—particularly in the motor and complex mental function domains. This differentiation impairment—more conspicuous for some functions than for others—resulted in different developmental trends for different functions in the retardates.

Thus the subgroup characteristics which were indicated in the normals were less distinct in the retardates. In spite of greater across-trait variability the retardates tended to be classified by general performance level. They tended to a certain fuzzy kind of similarity which appeared as a compromise between similarity and difference. Since the test factors seemed to be the same in the retardates and normals, only the emphasis was changed, and the differences appeared to be more quantitative than qualitative.

The general, rather than the specific impairment, did not provide for highly differentiated subgroups; for instance, related to etiology. Therefore the etiological data, and the lack of success with the inverse factor analysis and the syndrome analysis, supported the view of the generally operating factor or factors.

In this perplexing exposure there were some landmarks that lent distinction, to some extent, to subgroups of retardates, but primarily to the general ability structure of the retardates. The landmarks were, Pure Tone Threshold, Lower Arm Movement, The RTs, and Railwalking, which were heavy contributors to a higher across-trait variability. Low score on these variables was attributed to a variety of functions: attention, motivation or alertness, response initiation, effort or drive, fine motor coordination, and integration of gross motor movement with visual cues. It seemed that these characteristics embraced a number of functions, and therefore they did not come out in the traditional factor analysis as a single factor. In other words, even within the retarded syndrome there was difference in emphasis on what was impaired.

Thus it seemed that Pure Tone Threshold, Lower Arm Movement, and RTs—their levels, their difference in level from Speech and from complex motor tasks respectively, and their high correlation with complex mental functions—afforded the best clues to some of the basic characteristics of the retardates; traits which seemed to be uniformly found in retardates, regardless of etiology. In addition, there was a tendency for subjects with neurological impairment to have low performance level for Grip and Pegboard, and for subjects with clearly abnormal EEG to have impairment of interpretation of abstract concepts (such as span of apprehension), sustained attention, foresight and planning, and task attitude.

At this point one may compare the present findings with the seven objectives of the study which were stated in the Introduction.

1. It may be said that normative data for basic psychological functions have been assembled for a wide variety of tasks which in the past have not been systematically investigated among the mentally retarded.
2. New understanding of the basic characteristics of the mentally retarded has been provided and their structure of ability has been related to chronological and mental age.
3. The differentiation of the mentally retarded into subgroups which are psychologically and behaviorally more homogeneous than those provided by current classification systems has not been particularly successful. The outline of some broad groups has been presented, but well defined, specific groups have not been encountered.
4. The finding of relationship between configuration of abilities and extent of central nervous system damage—as indicated by med-

ical, neurological, and EEG examinations—has been only moderately successful. Only the more severe impairment seems to have been reflected in a few variables.

5. With limited success in defining homogeneous subgroups, the attempts to demonstrate relationships between these groups and traditional etiological groups have not been very productive.
6. It can hardly be said that new diagnostic tools have been developed, but some of the tests in the battery have distinguished themselves as being particularly sensitive indicators of retardation.
7. Extension and improvement of instrumentation for discriminating between individuals within subgroups cannot be said to have been achieved, because of the difficulties encountered in connection with defining subgroups.

It appears, then, that the key variables in the test battery are pure tone threshold and simple motor tasks—such as lower arm movement, simple reaction time, and railwalking. Not only are they the distinguishing traits for two subgroups but they are the characteristic features of an unselected retarded population. They are the major aspects which make the ability profiles of the retarded samples similar, and which differentiate them from the normals. Hence, it is believed that their interpretation is important for the understanding of retardate functioning.

From the data presented it seems clear that low pure tone threshold does not always reflect genuine hearing loss. Low pure tone threshold is often found where speech threshold is very close to normal. Similarly, poor performance level for simple motor tasks has been found where more complex tasks have been executed quite well—i.e., Hand Precision. As compared to pure tone, the stimulus for speech threshold is more complex in terms of frequency of the sound; it is more varied, interesting, and meaningful to the subject. Thus pure tone threshold may be more demanding with respect to effort. Simple RT differs from Lower Arm in terms of a reactive component, but the similarity in performance level of the two tasks in contrast to tapping performance suggests that both tasks depend heavily upon willingness to exert oneself to initiate a movement. The common denominator in the key tests seems to be of motivational nature, manifesting itself as sustained vigilance or attention on the one hand, and the more temporary initiation of movement on the other.

It seems unreasonable that complexity per se is responsible for the better performance. Rather, complexity probably operates indirectly, arousing greater interest and thus increasing the willingness to assert oneself, resulting in higher performance level. If this be the case, the low performance on simple motor tasks (Lower Arm and RTs) and pure tone threshold does not indicate impaired functions, but rather the absence of sufficient stimuli to maintain an arousal level adequate for the task. Thus the retardates may depend more heavily upon external stimulation than do the normals. Arousal level is probably not sufficient to explain all types of motor deficiencies in retardates, and eventually the general relationship between arousal and motor efficiency has to be investigated separately. It is possible that motor efficiency in relation to task complexity describes an inverted U-shaped curve, where deficiency for the simplest task is a result of arousal mechanism, while deficiencies for complex tasks result from impaired muscular coordination. Another lead to consider–as will be discussed later–is the brain stem reticular formation which seems to be involved in muscle tone as well as arousal. In his review article, King (1965 b) reported increase in muscular tension in psychopathological and geriatric subjects accompanying reduced psychomotor effectiveness. If our speculation of the role of arousal in certain groups of retardates is correct, one may expect that in these subjects there is decreased muscular tension. Thus a possibility exists that the retarded and psychopathological subjects tend to fall on opposite sides of normals with respect to arousal and muscular tension.

The possibility that motor deficiency in retarded subjects may be related to other factors than response initiation and muscle tension should be kept in mind, since Glanville and Kreezer (1937) reported that compared to normals a group of retarded subjects showed impairment for maximum amplitude of movement in various joints. Kreezer (1935) found the chronaxy of the triceps to vary inversely with MA. The retarded subjects examined by these authors were adults with MA from 9.0 to 9.9 years, of varied etiology and of no special clinical type. Kreezer concluded that "qualitative investigation of motor phenomena at different physiological levels brings to light distinct differences between the mentally normal and the feeble-minded. . . ."

Our concern with regard to functional impairment of certain groups of retardates seems therefore to be directed toward vigilance and response initiation. This implies that, for the majority of the retardates included in this study, the chief characteristic is probably some diffuse CNS impairment affecting the motivational aspect of behavior. This is not to deny the existence of localized lesions as they do exist in some retarded subjects, but such subjects are not included in the present study. One is reminded of Lashley's statement (1929, p. 118) "All of this points to the conclusion that defects of the maze habit are due to some general deterioration which affects the associative mechanism as a whole rather than distinct, qualitatively different, elements of the habit."

Spivack and Levine (1962) have also speculated that motivational and attentional factors may play a decisive role in sensory discriminatory performance of brain damaged children. Another finding which seems to support this point of view is that of Zeaman, House, and Orlando (1958), who found that introduction of novel stimuli, either positive or negative, can facilitate discrimination learning.

House and Zeaman (1961) reported that imbecile children of MA 2 to 5 years remained unaffected by practice in contrast to monkeys, when subjected to a two-choice spatial delayed-response task. Absence of delay learning set, through position habit and trace-perseveration error, was related to a deficit in attentive functions of the retardates. This finding, as well as findings from their earlier studies (1958, 1959), was interpreted to indicate that imbecile subjects are particularly deficient in directing and maintaining attention to relevant discrimination cues.

Recently, Zeaman and House (1963) have presented a more formal theory of the role of attention in discrimination learning in retardates. The theory states that the difficulties retardates have in discrimination learning is related to limitation in attending to the relevant stimulus dimension rather than limitation in approaching the correct cue of the stimulus dimension. Some of their assumptions and some of the implications stated in their work are at variance with those of the present study. While the general orientation is similar, it is difficult to say where the two studies support or contradict each other.

These authors (1958) have reported the following observation: "A subject who had failed a simple color-form discrimination for over 1000 trials, spontaneously went to a bench containing some 20 different stimuli and selected the two which had been used for the 1000 trials." This may be regarded as a situation similar to the discrepancy between pure tone and speech threshold. The retardates failed in the discrimination of pure tone task, not because of impaired discrimination or hearing, but because they were unable to maintain a sufficient level of attention to act in accordance with their potential.

Two recent studies have been directly concerned with vigilance in retardates. Ware, Baker, and Sipowicz (1962) investigated the monitoring of brief sporadic interruptions of a continuously presented light source on a group of 14 trainable subjects. For one condition of their experiment—no knowledge of results—they compared the data to findings of 14 normals from a previous study. No significant difference was found, but it is not clear how comparable the two studies are with respect to experimental conditions or subject characteristics. Semmel (1965) used a similar procedure to record vigilance performance—which he regarded as a manifestation of arousal—on 42 retarded children (Mean IQ 67.6) and 42 normal children (Mean IQ 105.5). As compared to the normals, the retarded children had significantly lower total vigilance scores; they were inferior in vigilance at each successive period of the experiment; and they revealed an earlier and more rapid decrement in vigilance behavior. Contrary to expectation, neither interpolated rest periods nor the introduction of a "novelty-condition"—extinction for 10 sec. of the signal source, followed by a bright red light—had any significant effects on the vigilance performance. In an unpublished presentation, Semmel has suggested that retarded children may need more environmental stimulation than do average children in order to produce maximum behavior efficiency.

While we have seen that Syndrome Types 2 and 3 differ somewhat in distribution over etiological categories, neurological impairment, and EEG abnormality, it has also been found that all three subgroups include all categories of etiology, neurological impairment, and EEG abnormality. The impairment in a substantial proportion of the retardates must therefore be of such a nature that it may have resulted from a variety of causes—e.g., prematurity, toxic agents, infections, trauma, metabolic errors, and perhaps environmental deprivation.

It is interesting to note that Teuber, Battersby, and Bender (1960), in studying the effect on the visual field of missile wounds in the brain, found extensive functional consequences from seemingly focal lesions. They were not able, however, to decide whether this was a result of diffuseness of lesion or if (p. 116) ". . . the functions in all parts of the field depend on the integrity of every individual part."

Our findings with the retardates seem to have some practical consequences which merit some comments before venturing into speculations about neurophysiological correlates of the behavioral characteristics. The first is a further comment with respect to terminology. The individuals with which we are concerned are called mentally retarded but there is not universal satisfaction with this term. Some prefer the term exceptional children, while others—e.g., Sarason and

Gladwin (1959)—have found that it lacks in precision. As an alternative, they have suggested that the term mentally deficient be used for those (p. 625) ". . . who have demonstrable central nervous system pathology of a kind and to a degree which probably rules out normal social and intellectual functioning." Mental retardation is used for the ". . . large groups of individuals whose retardation is not associated with organic pathology and who are able, or could become able, to maintain themselves in the community." In spite of the difference in organic pathology of the two groups, our data suggest that this distinction is not warranted because of their functional similarity. We therefore prefer to restrict the term mental retardation to those individuals usually found in the public education system who eventually reach a normal level of functioning—e.g., the so-called slow learner. Thus mental deficiency seems a more appropriate term for institutionalized populations where inferior performance in relation to age norm is permanent and not just delayed development.

A second comment refers to the classroom situation for the retardates. In contrast to the present findings, Werner and Thuma (1942 a and b), Werner and Strauss (1940, 1941), and Strauss and Werner (1941, 1942 a and b) found distinct differences between familial and organic subjects. We have already accounted for the discrepancy as having been caused by degree of impairment between their subjects and ours. Strauss and Lehtinen (1947) in discussing the training of brain injured children gave certain recommendations for classroom organization and teaching material. Since the children they discussed often are characterized by being distractible, hyperactive and restless, it was recommended that the classroom be kept barren and material be presented in relative isolation, to prevent distraction. Because of the paucity of substantial educational research in mental retardation, these ideas seem to have been applied more widely than the results warranted. The present findings and interpretations as to the lack of attentiveness and vigilance in many retarded subjects indicate that these individuals would benefit from stimulating surroundings in the classroom. In spite of the fact that some groups of retardates may require special techniques, it seems probable that a large group of them are not so functionally unique that other specialized techniques are warranted. To resolve such questions, educational research is gravely needed.

Related to the point of decreased arousal is a comment about the tasks which the retardates are given in a work situation, such as a sheltered workshop program. They are usually asked to do the most simple tasks with the danger that task monotony interfere with work output. If one of the cardinal problems of the retardates is to stimulate himself to initiate a movement, it may be defeating the purpose of the sheltered workshop program to use tasks which easily become boring. This will in many instances be a difficult problem to overcome as the variety of suitable complex tasks may be limited.

POSSIBLE NEUROPHYSIOLOGICAL CORRELATES

Since Moruzzi and Magoun in 1949 observed that electrical stimulation of the reticular formation in the cat resulted in generalized disorganization of cortical electrical activity, the reticular activating system has been studied intensely by physiologists and psychologists alike. The importance attributed to this system may be seen from the following statement by French (1960):

> It now appears likely that the brain-stem reticular formation represents one of the more important integrating structures if not, indeed, the master control mechanism in the central nervous system. Neuron combinations here long have been known to mediate the control of many visceral functions, such as respiration, vasomotor tone, and gastrointestinal secretion, and in recent years investigations have indicated participation of this region in neural processes subserving temperature regulation and neuroendocrine control. Furthermore, information has been adduced recently which assigns to the reticular formation a major role in the mediation of three more general neurola functions. First, it is known to be implicated in the arousal response and wakefulness. Second, it exerts a critical degree of influence over motor functions concernd in phasic and tonic muscular control. Third, the central brain stem is capable of modifying the reception, conduction and integration of all sensory signals to the degree that some will be perceived and others rejected by the nervous system.

The concepts involved result from the more flexible neurophysiological approach which developed with electroencephalography and which seems more appropriate for the variability and complexity of psychological processes. (For general references see Magoun, 1958; Lindsley, 1957, 1960; Jasper, 1958; and Samuels, 1959.)

The reticular formation comprises two different functional systems; the brain stem reticular formation and the diffuse or unspecific thalamocortical projection system. Originating in the brain stem, reticular formation is the dense network of the ascending reticular activating system (ARAS), part of which extends to the cortex via the internal capsule while the rest extends to the hypothalamus, subthalamus, and thalamus. The diffuse thalamocortical projection system (DTPS) is anatomically and functionally closely related to the ARAS. It originates in the nonspecific thalamic nuclei from which extensive and diffuse cortical projections develop. Included in the system are corticofugal fibers which project from the cortex to the reticular formation of the medulla. The DTPS has been so named to distinguish it from the specific thalamic projection system which is made up of projections from classical sensory relay nuclei to specific cortical areas. There is a close relationship between these systems, as collaterals from specific sensory pathways lead into the reticular formation on all levels. Also the corticofugal fibers afford regulation in terms of facilitation and inhibition of transmission along the sensory pathways. Descending fibers from the reticular formation enter the spinal cord and regulate postural and motor activity of skeletal musculature.

Stimulation of the brain stem and thalamic reticular system results in arousal. Electrophysiologically this means desynchronization of resting alpha rhythms throughout the cortex. Behaviorally it appears as increased alertness or as awaking in a sleeping animal. Destruction of the brain stem reticular formation results in somnolence and the animal can be aroused only slightly and momentarily. With brain stem reticular formation destroyed, impulses from the sensory pathways still reach the cortex but the stimuli do not seem to be perceived. With sensory projection paths transected but brain stem reticular formation intact, the animals show behavioral and electrophysiologic signs of arousal over sustained periods of time. Specific and nonspecific afferent fibers do not terminate on the same cells in the sensory cortex. The mechanism appears to be that nonspecific volleys facilitate interneurons on which the specific fibers terminate. According to Lindsley (1960), Hernandes-Peon and Hagbarth have shown that specific afferent and corticofugal impulses interact in the reticular formation resulting in either inhibition or facilitation of response to the stimulus. A difference between the brain stem and thalamic reticular systems appears to be that whereas the former serves the general arousal, the latter seems to mediate a more differentiated state of attention to a stimulus. The general arousal mechanism seems to be the more powerful of the two.

The flexibility, complexity, and extensiveness of the systems outlined above provide possible neurophysiological counterparts to a number of components of behavior. A series of quotes will serve to indicate how important these mechanisms are regarded to be. "Ingram, summarizing experiments done with Knott and others, reported that bilateral destruction of dorsomedial thalamic nuclei slows performance rate and retards learning in the cat, but that lesion of the nucleus centromedian had no such effects" (Lindsley, 1960, p. 1566). Hernandes-Peon et al. (1956) referring to conditioned salivation concluded that "learning seems to require the functional integrity of the brain stem reticular formation." "The neurophysiological distinction between 'specific' and 'non-specific' systems is particularly relevant to psychological theory. Constructs such as attention, perception, motivation, drive, reward, and punishment possess a common factor of non-specific reticular activitation in addition to their specific properties" and "the importance of these cortical connections can scarcely be over-emphasized, for they provide a means whereby the cortex can control the activating mechanisms of the brain stem and thus influence its own level of arousal." (Samuels, 1959). Of particular interest is a quotation which Lindsley (1957, p. 69) cites from French, Hernandes-Peon, and Livingston: "It seems logical to conclude that under normal physical conditions influences exerted upon the reticular activating system by these specific cortical zones may be functionally allied to arousal. For consideration in this regard is the possibility that these cortico-subcortical mechanisms might participate in such aspects of consciousness as voluntary alerting, vigilance or perhaps 'set' and meditation or introspection."

Considering the intricate and extensive implications of the reticular system, it would seem that impairment to these structures by necessity would make the individual appear retarded. In discussing the "de-synchronization" or "differentiation" of EEG patterns, which takes place when a person is alerted or aroused, Lindsley (1957, p. 79-80) made the following statement: "The process of 'differentiation,' which seems to be necessary to perception and the formation of habits and also in the intellectual application of these, may be a process which is lacking or improperly timed in the mentally deficient person. It is conceivable that some innate property of organization of the ARAS is lacking in such persons; . . ." According to Gibbs and Gibbs (1962), Lindsley in 1961 repeated the suggestion that damage to the reticular formation may be responsible for some types of mental retardation.

It is interesting to note that at a conference at The Training School at Vineland, T. C. Ruch (1958) also suggested impairment of ARAS as a cause of dullness.

It should be realized that, like the subconscious of an earlier era, the reticular formation today may be called upon to explain all shades of behavior without there being a demonstrable relationship. In spite of this, it appears that the "General Ability" type of retardates may be a result of more or less slight impairment of the ARAS system resulting in hypofunction. The basic arguments, which have already been presented, are the generality of impaired performance level, the independence of etiological category, and lack of relationship to neurological impairment and EEG abnormality. It is assumed that slight impairment of the ARAS system would make a less efficient arousal mechanism resulting in generally impaired performance on all tasks. Such a diffuse mechanism of impairment is in harmony with independence of etiological categories and lack of specific neurological impairment. It is puzzling that the General Ability group did not include individuals with rather low performance levels. The other two retarded types that appeared to be indicated in our data were both characterized by low performance levels, particularly for pure tone threshold and/or simple motor tasks. It is believed that in addition to the ARAS impairment in these groups there is impairment of the corticofugal connections, with the result that signals from the cortex are not available for regulation of arousal. Thus these individuals are lacking sustained attention, voluntary control of effort, and response initiation. Simple motor tasks and pure tone threshold are consequently more vulnerable while complex motor tasks and threshold for speech have more intrinsic arousal value allowing signals from the regular sensory collaterals to regulate arousal.

It is tempting to speculate further that the basis for the hyperactive, distractible retarded child is hyperfunction of the ARAS or DTPS even though they do not seem to constitute a homogeneous subgroup in the present study. In this connection, Hebb (1955) has suggested that there is an optimal level of arousal for effective behavior. Too low or too high a level of arousal will interfere with the cue function of the sensory systems. In a recent article Berkson (1961) reviewed studies which concerned responsiveness in the mentally retarded as indicated by reflexes, EEG frequency, alpha block latency and duration, GSR, startle reflex, and reaction time. He concluded that retardates respond less intensely and for a shorter duration than do normals. They do not differ with respect to speed of physiological responses, but have slower voluntary responses. This slowness may be related to the generally low responsiveness which may affect the learning process. These conclusions are in general agreement with the present findings, but the area of physiological responses in the retardates has not been sufficiently investigated.

In discussing the correlation and the traditional factor analysis, it was observed that there is closer relationship between mental and physical functions in the retardates than in the normals. In this connection, it is interesting to observe that even before the recent work relating it to arousal, the reticular formation's function for vascular control and muscle tone was well known. An interference with this system could easily affect both mental and physical functions giving the appearance of a closer correspondence between the two. This suggests an explanation for the lesser differentiation (higher correlation) in the retardates than the normals, especially between motor and intellectual functions.

It may be of interest to relate the position taken in this discussion to the viewpoints and findings of Russian investigators.

Luria's (1961 a and b, 1963) point of departure was children who fail in school. These children he separated into the following categories: educationally backward children, truly feeble-minded children, asthenic children, and children with partial defects. It is only the "truly feeble-minded" category which is of concern here, and which he further separated into (a.) individuals with residual of general brain disease resulting in generally arrested development, (b.) individuals where feeble-mindedness was complicated by neurodynamic disturbances, and (c.) individuals with additional focal syndrome.

While it is difficult to relate our behavioral indices to Luria's, it appears our General Ability Group corresponds to his category of generally arrested development. More questionable, but still a possibility, is that our subgroups with particular deficiency in pure tone and/or simple motor tasks correspond to his category of neurodynamic disturbance (imbalance of excitation-inhibition). (See also Pevzner, 1963.) One technique used to diagnose these categories was an objective method utilizing the orienting reflex (OR) to separate sensory defects from defects in attention and understanding. The orienting reflex is the organism's normal reaction to a stimulus, manifested by changes in EEG, galvanic skin resistance, constriction of blood vessels, and other autonomic reactions. Its manifestation in the vascular system is a disparate one, a dilation of the blood vessels of the head and a constriction of the digital blood vessels. This distinguishes it from the defense reaction which results in a constriction of the blood vessels in both areas. After repeated application of the same stimulus, habituation occurs. If, however, a slight change is made in the stimulus, the OR reappears.

The OR may be made more stable by asking the child to press a button at each sound or count its number (signalling function). This makes the child attend to the sound signal rather than to irrelevant stimuli. The normal child is characterized by a stable OR and active attention. In the imbecile child an active process is not established, and after two or three repetitions the vascular reaction is exhausted. But a novel stimulus again creates an intense reaction in these children. Thus it is demonstrated that the imbecile child is not attending. To investigate the understanding ability, the same technique was used with words instead of sounds. Normal subjects having learned to respond to a particular word will respond with an OR to words of similar meaning but not to words of similar sound. In other words, semantic generalization but not sound generalization is established. The imbecile child tends to show sound generalization but only weak semantic generalization because understanding is impaired. It appears that the OR is quite often lacking or interfered with in feeble-minded children and thus has considerable theoretical and practical clinical significance. Evidence, however, for it is as yet very meager (Razran, 1961); and outside of Russia there has been little concern with this approach until recently.

To summarize, Luria has shown that the OR of the feeble-minded is impaired, in that they do not pay sustained attention to stimuli, while we have preferred to express such lack of attention in terms of impaired arousal regulated by the reticular formation. We have indicated two or three subgroups which seemed to have varied with respect to degree of reticular formation impairment. Apparently Luria has not reported differences in pattern of OR which were implied by his descriptions of the three clinical subgroups of the "truly feeble-minded."

It is interesting to note that both the OR and arousal are alerting responses to external stimuli. EEG pattern, which is regarded as the best indicator of arousal, is also used to indicate the OR and autonomic activity as well as arousal. It seems reasonable to conclude that the OR and the reticular formation approaches to mental retardation have much in common. According to Razran (1961) there have been attempts by both Anokhin and Sokolov to relate the orienting reflex to the action of the reticular formation. Recently, Luria (1963) has interpreted the OR in terms of reticular formation. How much these two concepts do have in common and how they are related to our behavioral data would best be investigated by comparing these measures in a single group of retarded subjects.

In current investigations of this laboratory, Karrer and Clausen (1964) have found indications that some retardates have low GSR resting level and less reactivity to sound (56 db) than do normal subjects. The tendency to be less reactive may be interpreted in terms of low arousal level in the retardates and consistent with Luria's finding of impaired orienting reflex. Other aspects of the data, however, are not consistent with such an interpretation. It is possible that even greater differentiation between normals and retardates would have been obtained if less intense stimuli had been used—in other words, if greater demand had been made on the arousal mechanism.

Another approach which may be considered in this connection is Hebb's (1949) theory of organization of behavior. A general theory of behavior must be able to explain the deviant characteristics of mental retardation. The stress that is placed on the integrative processes in the formation of superstructures and their significance for learning would seem a particularly appropriate explanation for the intellectual limitation characteristic of the retardates. Benoit (1957, 1959, 1960) has advocated the relevance of Hebb's theory for mental retardation. There are, however, reasons why at this stage one should refrain from a discussion of the present results in terms of Hebb's theory. The finding of relatively better performance in the retardates for complex than for simple motor activities and generally better performance for perceptual than for motor tasks indicates that problems other than integration were also involved—e.g., arousal. In a later article Hebb (1955) has stressed the importance of the reticular system, and the possibility that the conditions for the integration may be understood in terms of the arousal system. Having pointed out the importance of a difference between the specific and the non-specific systems, he says: "Without the arousal system, the sensory impulses by the direct route reach the sensory cortex, but go no farther; the rest of the cortex is unaffected, and thus learned stimulus response relations are lost." He suggested that arousal be regarded as synonymous with a general drive state, which tones up the cortex and upon which all learning is dependent. Regardless of these statements there is no systematic incorporation of reticular formation function in his theory, and until this is accomplished it is difficult to relate our finding to cell assembly theory.

Thus it appears that if we are to understand some fundamental problems of the mentally retarded, we shall have to come to grips with motivational functions, particularly arousal functions of the organism.

If the interpretations of the present data are correct, it is likely that muscle tone and vascular function may show aberration in the retardates. Thus the possibility exists that some retardates may have deviant patterns of autonomic and somatic activity, and that these may be used as indicators of the arousal mechanism.

Kinesthetic functions have on several occasions indicated their presence but their significance remained unclear. Samuels (1959) stated that "Nociception and proprioception have been found to induce the most intense and widespread cortical activation, with auditory and visual stimuli producing the least." It seems, therefore, to be indicated that further attention should be given to kinesthetic functions in future work.

To explain certain subgroups of mental retardation as a result of malfunction of the reticular formation is not more than to speculate at the present stage. Information about the properties and functions of the reticular system seems at the present time to have been obtained largely from animal experiments in which substantial impairment had been induced. Clinical cases with reticular impairment do not seem to have been discussed. It is possible that clinical cases should be sought particularly among the retarded. It would be a mistake, however, to extend these suggestions too far. There are retarded individuals who, in spite of their intellectual limitations, appear to be alert and responsive. It should also be remembered that the criteria of IQ and functional impairment for inclusion in this study were restrictive, and that only the three subgroups arising from the factor and syndrome analysis were considered as implicating the reticular formation.

Further studies of these problems may take two avenues. The first is to study the arousal mechanism (including vigilance and habituation) in retardates as compared to normals. According to Lindsley (1960) the most direct way of studying arousal is by recording the desynchronization of EEG pattern in response to stimuli. Rather than the traditional measures of frequency, amplitude, or percent time alpha, the modification of the EEG pattern as a result of activation and the 4-7 per sec theta waves would be the best indicators. Lansing, Schwartz, and Lindsley (1959) have demonstrated the relationship between alpha blocking and reaction time and believe that both reduced RT and EEG activation may be identified with arousal. Autonomic responses to stimulation could also be used as there would seem to be a relationship between arousal and sympathetic activity.

Another approach would be to produce "mental retardation" in animals by subjecting them to conditions or treatments which are known to result in mental retardation in humans. In such animals degree of "retardation" and reticular formation impairment could be appraised by standard psychological and neurophysiological methods. In this connection it may be noted that several studies have been reported where "retardation" has been produced by anoxia (Saxon, 1961; Windle, 1963), chemical agents (Waisman, 1963; Karrer and Cahilly, 1965) and environmental conditions (Krech, Rosenzweig, and Bennett, 1962). The research program of this institution, designed to investigate the relationships between biological mechanisms and behavioral manifestation, has been described elsewhere (Clausen, Rendina, Karrer, and Cahilly, 1964).

The results of the Ability Structure Project tend to emphasize the generality of impairment in a particular group of retarded subjects. Even more extensive has been the significance of functions which have been related to the arousal mechanism: immediate attention, sustained attention, effort, and response initiation. Early investigators and clinicians in the field of mental retardation have expressed points of view which do not differ substantially from this. Binet and Simon (1916) suggested that concentration, which appears to be synonymous with attention, is organized in a hierarchical pattern: awakening of concentration, maintenance of concentration, return to original object after distraction, and resistance to distraction. Impairment of this function is characteristic for the retardates, with a relationship between level of disturbed attention (as described in the hierarchical pattern) and intellectual functioning. They regarded as of greater importance the incapacity of all retardates to muster voluntary effort. Goddard (1919) revealed the importance he assigned to attention by the statement that "The stimulus arouses the consciousness and that consciousness is the attention" (p. 77) and ". . . attention is only a name of the *maximum consciousness* at any given moment and is dependent upon the character of the stimulus and the neuron pattern" (p. 78). He distinguished between instinctive or inherited attention which results from an inherited neuron pattern, and acquired attention which is an extension of the instinctive attention. Lack of acquired attention was regarded as a characteristic of the feeble-minded. ". . . he attends to those things that appeal to him instinctively. But those things that depend for the arousal of consciousness, which means attention, upon the combinations of elaborate neuron patterns based upon experience, he cannot do" (p. 108). Tredgold (1947) expressed concern that defect of attention and recall had been overemphasized as characteristics of retardation. He adopted the opposite view that "The defective child does not register, and therefore cannot retain things, because he is not interested in them; or he does not understand, and consequently does not attend to them" (p. 94). Thus he saw attention defects as result rather than cause for mental retardation.

It appears that during the last 50 years psychologists have been less concerned with the problem of attention. The reason may be that the concept of attention has been a difficult one to handle experimentally, and with measuring tools for other functions being more readily supplied, other avenues have become more tempting. Investigators of mental retardation shifted their concern from a deficiency which permeated all actions, to a concern for the more specific disabilities which may be related to more focal CNS impairments.

The consideration of a large number of variables in the present study has given us experimental evidence for the significance of these old concepts relative to the role of attention and voluntary effort in retardation. Recent advances in neurophysiology seem to offer a neurophysiological substrate for those functions under the common heading of arousal. This makes it possible to put the concepts to more stringent tests than ever before. While such investigation will not solve all the problems in the field, it offers to significantly increase our knowledge concerning mental retardation.

VI REFERENCES

Attenborough, Joan & Farber, Miriam. The relation between intelligence, mechanical ability and manual dexterity in special school children. *Brit. J. educ. Psychol.*, 1934, *4*, 140-161.

Atwell, W. O. & Elbel, E. R. Reaction time of male high school students in 14-17 year age groups. *Res. Quart. Amer. Assoc. Hlth. Phys. Educ.*, 1948, *19*, 22-29.

Baldwin, B. T. *Physical growth of children from birth to maturity.* University of Iowa Studies in Child Welfare. Vol. I, No. 1. Iowa City: Univ. of Iowa, 1921.

Barnett, C. D., Ellis, N. R., & Pryer, Margaret W. Learning in familial and brain-injured defectives. *Amer. J. ment. Defic.*, 1960, *64*, 894-901.

Baroff, G. S. WISC patterning in endogenous mental deficiency. *Amer. J. ment. Defic.*, 1959, *64*, 482-485.

Beck, H. S. & Lam, R. L. Use of the WISC in predicting organicity. *J. clin. Psychol.*, 1955, *11*, 154-158.

Bellis, Carrole J. Reaction time and chronological age. *Proc. Soc. Exp. Biol. & Med.*, 1933, *30*, 801-803.

Benoit, E. P. Relevance of Hebb's theory of the organization of behavior to educational research on the mentally retarded. *Amer. J. ment. Defic.*, 1957, *61*, 497-507.

Benoit, E. P. Toward a new definition of mental retardation. *Amer. J. ment. Defic.*, 1959, *63*, 559-565.

Benoit, E. P. Application of Hebb's theory to understanding the learning disability of children with mental retardation. *Train. Sch. Bull.*, 1960, *57*, 18-23.

Bensberg, G. J. & Cantor, G. N. Reaction time in mental defectives with organic and familial etiology. *Amer. J. ment. Defic.*, 1957, *62*, 534-537.

Benton, A. L., Jentsch, R. C. & Wahler, H. J. Simple and choice reaction times in schizophrenia. *A.M.A. Arch. Neurol. Psychiat.*, 1959, *81*, 373-376.

Berkson, G. An analysis of reaction time in normal and mentally deficient young men. I. Duration threshold experiment. *J. ment. Defic. Res.*, 1960, *4*, 51-58. (a)

Berkson, G. An analysis of reaction time in normal and mentally deficient young men. II. Variation of complexity in reaction time task. *J. ment. Defic. Res.*, 1960, *4*, 59-67. (b)

Berkson, G. An analysis of reaction time in normal and mentally deficient young men. III. Variation of stimulus and of response complexity. *J. ment. Defic. Res.*, 1960, *4*, 69-77 (c)

Berkson, G. Responsiveness of the mentally deficient. *Amer. J. ment. Defic.*, 1961, *66*, 277-286.

Berlyne, D. E. Recent developments in Piaget's work. *Brit. J. educ. Psychol.*, 1957, *27*, 1-12.

Binet, A. & Simon, T. *The intelligence of the feeble-minded.* Publ. of Train. Sch. at Vineland, N. J. Baltimore: Williams & Wilkins, 1916.

Birch, J. W. & Matthews, J. The hearing of mental defectives: its measurement and characteristics. *Amer. J. ment. Defic.,* 1951, *55*, 384-393.

Blackburn, H. L. & Benton, A. L. Simple and choice reaction time in cerebral disease. *Conf. Neurol.*, 1955, *15*, 327-338.

Bolduc, T. E. Social value-need patterns in mental retardates. *J. consult. Psychol.*, 1960, *24*, 472-479.

Cantor, G. N. & Stacey, C. L. Manipulative dexterity in mental defectives. *Amer. J. ment. Defic.*, 1951, *56*, 401-410.

Cassel, Margaret E. & Riggs, Margaret M. Comparison of three etiological groups of mentally retarded children on the Vineland Social Maturity Scale. *Amer. J. ment. Defic.*, 1953, *58*, 162-169.

Clarke, Ann M. & Clarke, A. D. B. *Mental deficiency—The changing outlook.* Glencoe, Ill.: The Free Press, 1958.

Clausen, J. An evaluation of experimental methods of time judgment. *J. exp. Psychol.*, 1950, *40*, 756-761.

Clausen, J. PMA subscores in retardates and normals: pattern, scatter, correlations, and relation to etiology. *Amer. J. ment. Defic.*, 1965, *70*, 232-247.

Clausen, J. & Karrer, R. Electrical sensitivity of the eye in the mentally retarded. *Train. Sch. Bull.*, 1961, *58*, 3-13.

Clausen, J. & Karrer, R. Comparison of phosphene threshold to various visual functions and to electrical sensitivity of the skin. *J. Psychol.*, 1963, *55*, 91-99.

Clausen, J., Rendina, G., Karrer, R. & Cahilly, G. The research program at the Training School at Vineland, New Jersey. *Train. Sch. Bull.*, 1964, *61*, 49-64.

Clinton, R. J. Nature of mirror-drawing ability: norms on mirror-drawing for white children by age and sex. *J. educ. Psychol.*, 1930, *21*, 221-228.

Coghill, G. E. Individuation versus integration in the development of behavior. *J. gen. Psychol.*, 1930, *3*, 431-435.

Cromwell, R. L. & Foshee, J. G. Studies in activity level: IV. Effects of visual stimulation during task performance in mental defectives. *Amer. J. ment. Defic.*, 1960, *65*, 248-251.

Cronbach, L. J. & Gleser, G. C. Assessing similarity between profiles. *Psychol. Bull.*, 1953, *50*, 456-473.

Cruse, D. B. Effects of distraction upon the performance of brain-injured and familial retarded children. *Amer. J. ment. Defic.*, 1961, *66*, 86-92.

Csank, J. Z. & Lehman, H. E. Developmental norms on four psychophysiological measures for use in the evaluation of psychotic disorders. *Cand. J. Psychol.*, 1958, *12*, 127-133.

Culbertson, Ellen, Guthrie, G. M., Butler, A. J., & Gorlow, L. Patterns of hostility among the retarded. *Amer. J. ment. Defic.*, 1961, *66*, 421-427.

Davis, H. & Silverman, S. R. *Hearing and deafness.* New York: Holt, Rinehart & Winston, 1960.

Distefano, M. K., Jr., Ellis, N. R., & Sloan, W. Motor proficiency in mental defectives. *Percept. mot. Skills*, 1958, *8*, 231-234.

Doll, E. A. Psychological significance of cerebral birth lesions. *Amer. J. Psychol.*, 1933, *45*, 444-452.

Doll, E. A. The feeble-minded child. In L. Carmichael (Ed.), *Manual of child psychology.* New York: John Wiley, 1946. Pp. 845-885.

Edwards, A. S. The measurement of static ataxia. *Amer. J. Psychol.*, 1942, *55*, 171-188.

Ellis, N. R. (Ed.) *Handbook of mental deficiency: Psychological theory and research.* New York: McGraw-Hill, 1963.

Ellis, N. R., Barnett, C. D. & Pryer, Margaret W. Performance of mental defectives on the mirror drawing task. *Percept. mot. Skills*, 1957, *7*, 271-274.

Ellis, N. R., Hawkins, W. F., Pryer, Margaret W. & Jones, R. W. Distraction effects in oddity learning by normal and mentally defective humans. *Amer. J. ment. Defic.*, 1963, *67*, 576-583.

Ellis, N. R. & Sloan, W. Relationship between intelligence and simple reaction time in mental defectives. *Percept. mot. Skills*, 1957, *7*, 65-67. (a)

Ellis, N. R. & Sloan, W. Rotary pursuit performance as a function of mental age. *Percept. mot. Skills*, 1957, *7*, 267-270. (b)

Eyman, R. K., Dingman, H. F., & Windle, C. Manipulative dexterity and movement history of mental defectives. *Percept. mot. Skills*, 1959, *9*, 291-294.

Eysenck, H. J. Classification and the problem of diagnosis. In H. J. Eysenck (Ed.), *Handbook of abnormal psychology, an experimental approach.* New York: Basic Books, 1961, Pp. 1-31.

Fait, H. F. & Kupferer, Harriet J. A study of two motor achievement tests and its implications in planning physical activities for the mentally retarded. *Amer. J. ment. Defic.*, 1956, *60*, 729-732.

Foale, Martha & Paterson, J. W. The hearing of mental defectives. *Amer. J. ment. Defic.*, 1954, *59*, 254-258.

Foshee, J. G. Studies in actvitity level: I. Simple and complex task performance in defectives. *Amer. J. ment. Defic.*, 1958, *62*, 882-896.

Francis, R. J. & Rarick, G. L. *Motor characteristics of the mentally retarded.* Coop. Res. Monogr. No. 1 (OE-35005). U. S. Dept. of HEW, Office of Education: Washington, 1960.

French, J. D. The reticular formation. In J. Field, H. W. Magoun & V. E. Hall (Eds.), *Handbook of Physiology,* Section 1: Neurophysiology, Vol. II. Washington: Amer. Physiol. Soc., 1960, Pp. 1281-1305.

Fruchter, B. *Introduction to factor analysis.* New York: D. Van Nostrand, 1954.

Gallagher, J. J. A comparison of brain-injured and non-brain injured mentally retarded children on several psychological variables. *Monogr. Soc. Res. Child Developm.*, 1957, *22*, No. 2.

Gardner, W. I., Cromwell, R. L., & Foshee, J. G. Studies in activity level: II. Effects of distal visual stimulation in organics, familials, hyperactives, and hypoactives. *Amer. J. ment. Defic.*, 1959, *63*, 1028-1033.

Garrison, M. A comparison of psychological measures in mentally retarded boys over a three-year period as a function of etiology. *Train. Sch. Bull.*, 1958, *55*, 54-60.

Gesell, A. Maturation and the patterning of behavior. In C. Murchison (Ed.), *A handbook of child psychology.* (2nd ed.) Worcester, Mass.: Clark Univ. Press, 1933.

Gibbs, E. L. & Gibbs, F. A. Extreme spindles: correlation of electroencephalographic sleep pattern with mental retardation. *Science,* 1962, *138*, 1106-1107.

Gilbert, J. A. *Researches on the mental and physical development of school children.* Studies from the Yale Psychological Laboratory, 1894, Vol. 2.

Gilbert, J. A. *Researches upon school children and college students.* Univ. of Iowa Studies in Psychology, 1897, Vol. I.

Glanville, A. D. & Kreezer, G. Deficiencies in amplitude of joint movement associated with mental deficiency. *Child Developm.*, 1937, *8*, 129-138.

Goddard, H. H. *Psychology of the normal and subnormal.* New York, N.Y.: Dodd, Mead & Co., 1919.

Goetzinger, C. P. A re-evaluation of the Heath Railwalking Test. *J. educ. Res.*, 1961, *54*, 187-191.

Goodenough, Florence L. The development of the reactive process from early childhood to maturity. *J. exp. Psychol.*, 1935, *18*, 431-450.

Goodenough, Florence L. *Developmental Psychology.* (2nd ed.) New York: Appleton-Century, 1945.

Guilford, J. P. Factorial angles to psychology. *Psychol. Rev.*, 1961, *68*, 1-20.

Guthrie, G. M., Butler, A., & Gorlow, L. Patterns of self-attitudes of retardates. *Amer. J. ment. Defic.*, 1961, *66*, 222-229.

Harris, A. J. *Harris Tests of Lateral Dominance.* Manual of directions. (2nd ed.) New York: Psych. Corp., 1955.

Hartmann, G. W. Comparison of the flicker thresholds in children and adults. *Child Developm.*, 1934, *5*, 122-126.

Heath, S. R., Jr. Rail-walking performance as related to mental age and etiological type among the mentally retarded. *Amer. J. Psychol.*, 1942, *55*, 240-247.

Heath, S. R., Jr. The rail-walking test: Preliminary maturational norms for boys and girls. *Mot. Skills Res. Exch.*, 1949, *1*, 34-36.

Hebb, D. O. *Organization of behavior.* New York: Wiley, 1949.

Hebb, D. O. Drive and the C.N.S. (conceptual nervous system). *Psychol. Rev.*, 1955, *62*, 243-254.

Hernandes-Peon, R., Brust-Carmona, H., Eckhaus, E., Lopez-Mendoza, E., & Alcocer-Cuaron, C. Functional role of brain stem reticular system in salivary conditioned response. *Fed. Proc.*, 1956, *15*, 91.

Hoakley, Z. Pauline & Frazeur, Helen A. Significance of psychological test results of exogenous and endogenous children. *Amer. J. ment. Defic.*, 1945, *50*, 263-271.

House, Betty J. & Zeaman, D. Reward and nonreward in the discrimination learning of imbeciles. *J. comp. physiol. Psychol.*, 1958, *51*, 614-618.

House, Betty J. & Zeaman, D. Position discrimination and reversals in low-grade retardates. *J. comp. physiol. Psychol.*, 1959, *52*, 564-565.

House, Betty J. & Zeaman, D. Effects of practice on the delayed response of retardates. *J. comp. physiol. Psychol.*, 1961, *54*, 255-260.

Hunt, Betty & Patterson, Ruth M. Performance of brain-injured and familial mentally deficient children on visual and auditory sequences. *Amer. J. ment. Defic.*, 1958, *63*, 72-80.

Hunter, W. S. & Sigler, M. The span of visual discrimination as a function of time and intensity of stimulation. *J. exp. Psychol.*, 1940, *26*, 160-179.

Jasper, H. Reticular-cortical systems and theories of the integrative action of the brain. In H. F. Harlow & C. N. Woolsey (Eds.), *Biological and biochemical bases of behavior.* Madison: Univ. of Wisconsin Press, 1958. Pp. 37-61.

Jenkin, N. & West, Noel I. Perception in organic mental defectives: An exploratory study. I. The size-weight illusion. *Train. Sch. Bull.*, 1958, *55*, 5-10.

Jenkin, N. & West, Noel I. Perception in organic mental defectives: An exploratory study. II. The Muller-Lyer illusion. *Train. Sch. Bull.*, 1959, *55*, 67-70.

Johnston, P. W. & Farrell, M. J. Auditory impairments among resident school children at the Walter E. Fernald State School. *Amer. J. ment. Defic.*, 1954, *58*, 640-643.

Jones, H. E. *Motor performance and growth.* Berkeley: Univ. of California Press, 1949.

Jordan, T. E. *The mentally retarded.* Columbus, Ohio: Charles E. Merrill, 1961.

Karrer, R. & Clausen, J. A comparison of mentally deficient and normal individuals upon four dimensions of autonomic activity. *J. ment. Defic., Res.*, 1964, *8*, 149-163.

Karrer, R. & Cahilly, G. Experimental attempts to produce phenylketonuria in animals: a critical review. *Psychol. Bull.*, 1965, *64*, 52-64.

King, H. E. *Psychomotor aspects of mental disease.* Cambridge, Mass.: Harvard Univ. Press, 1954.

King, H. E. Reaction time and speed of voluntary movement by normal and psychotic subjects. *J. Psychol.*, 1965, *59*, 219-227. (a)

King, H. E. Psychomotor changes with age, psychopathology and brain damage. In A. T. Welford & J. Birren (Eds.), *Behavior, aging, and the nervous system.* Springfield: Thomas, 1965. Pp. 476-525 (b)

King, H. E. & Clausen, J. Psychophysiology. In F. A. Mettler (Ed.), *Psychosurgical problems.* New York: Blakiston, 1952. Pp. 254-274.

King, H. E. & Clausen, J. Psychophysiology. In N. D. C. Lewis, C. Landis, & H. E. King (Eds.), *Studies in Topectomy.* New York: Grune and Stratton, 1956. Pp. 126-149.

Kratter, F. E. Color-blindness in relation to normal and defective intelligence. *Amer. J. ment. Defic.*, 1957, *62*, 436-441.

Krech, D., Rosenzweig, M. R. & Bennett, E. L. Relations between brain chemistry and problem-solving among rats raised in enriched and impoverished environments. *J. comp. physiol. Psychol.*, 1962, *55*, 801-807.

Kreezer, G. Motor studies of the mentally deficient: Quantitative methods at various levels of integration. *Train. Sch. Bull.*, 1935, *32*, 125-135.

Lacey, J. I. Psychophysiological approaches to the evaluation of psychotherapeutic process and outcome. In: *Research in psychotherapy.* Washington, D. C.: Amer. Psychol. Assoc., 1959. Pp. 160-208.

Lansing, R. W., Schwartz, E., & Lindsley, D. B. Reaction time and EEG activation under alerted and nonalerted conditions. *J. exp. Psychol.*, 1959, *58*, 1-7.

Lashley, K. S. *Brain mechanisms and intelligence.* Chicago: Univ. of Chicago Press, 1929.

Lewin, K. *A dynamic theory of personality.* New York: McGraw-Hill, 1935.

Lewin, K. Behavior and development as a function of the total situation. In L. Carmichael (Ed.), *Manual of child psychology.* New York: John Wiley, 1946. Pp. 791-844.

Lindsley, D. B. Psychophysiology and motivation. In M. R. Jones (Ed.), *Nebraska symposium on motivation.* Lincoln: Univ. Nebraska Press, 1957. Pp. 44-105.

Lindsley, D. B. Attention, consciousness, sleep and wakefulness. In J. Field, H. W. Magoun & V. E. Hall (Eds.), *Handbook of Physiology*, Section 1: Neurophysiology. Vol. III. Washington: Amer. Physiol. Soc., 1960. Pp. 1553-1593.

Luriya, A. R. An objective approach to the study of the abnormal child. *Amer. J. Orthopsychiat.*, 1961, *31*, 1-16. (a)

Luriya, A. R. The role of speech in the regulation of normal and abnormal behavior. J. Tizard (Ed.) New York: Liveright Publ. Co., 1961. (b)

Luriya, A. R. *The mentally retarded child (outlines of studies on the higher nervous activity characteristics of oligophrenic children).* Washington, D. C.: O.T.S., U.S. Depart. of Commerce, 1963.

McFarland, R. A., Warren, A. B., & Karis, C. Alterations in critical flicker frequency as a function of age and light: dark ratio. *J. exp. Psychol.*, 1958, *56*, 529-538.

McKinney, J. P. A multidimensional study of the behavior of severely retarded boys. *Child Developm.*, 1962, *33*, 923-938.

McMurray, J. G. Visual perception in exogenous and endogenous mentally retarded children. *Amer. J. ment. Defic.*, 1954, *58*, 659-663.

McQuitty, L. L. Elementary factor analysis. *Psychol. Rep.*, 1961, *9*, 71-78.

Magoun, H. W. Non-specific brain mechanisms. In H. F. Harlow & C. N. Woolsey (Eds.), *Biological and biochemical bases of behavior.* Madison: Univ. of Wisconsin Press, 1958. Pp. 25-36.

Malamud, N. Recent trends in classification of neuropathological findings in mental deficiency. *Amer. J. ment. Defic.*, 1954, *58*, 438-447.

Mark, H. J., Meier, P. & Pasamanick, B. Variability of critical flicker fusion thresholds in brain-injured children. *A.M.A. Arch. Neurol. Psychiat.*, 1958, *80*, 682-688.

Meili, R. & Tobler, E. Les mouvements stroboscopiques chez les enfants. *Arch. de Psychol, Geneve*, 1931, *23*, 131-156.

Meredith, H. V. *The rhythm of physical growth: A study of eighteen anthropometric measurements on Iowa City white males ranging in age between birth and eighteen years.* Univ. of Iowa Studies in Child Welfare, 1935.

Metheny, Eleanor. The present status of strength testing for children of elementary school and pre-school age. *Res. Quart. Amer. Assoc. Hlth. phys. Educ.*, 1941, *12*, 115-130.

Meyers, C. E. & Dingman, H. F. The structure of abilities at the preschool age: Hypothesized domains. *Psychol. Bull.*, 1960, *57*, 514-532.

Meyers, C. E. & Dingman, H. F. Factor analytic and structure of intellect; models in the study of mental retardation. Paper presented at the Conference on cognitive modals and development in mental retardation, Haddonfield, N. J., Nov. 19-21, 1964.

Meyers, C. E., Dingman, H. F., Attwell, A. A., & Orpet, R. E. Comparative abilities of normals and retardates of M.A. 6 years on a factor-type test battery. *Amer. J. ment. Defic.*, 1961, *66*, 250-258.

Meyers, C. E., Orpet, R. E., Attwell, A. A., & Dingman, H. F. Primary abilities at mental age six. *Monog. Soc. Res. Child Developm.* 1962, *27*, No. 1.

Miles, W. R. Static equilibrium. In R. W. Gerard (Ed.), *Methods in Medical Research*, Vol. 3. Chicago: Year Book Publ., 1950, Pp. 157-165.

Miller, V. L. The critical frequency limen for visual flicker in children between the ages of six and eighteen. *Genet. psychol. Monogr.*, 1942, *26*, 3-53.

Misiak, H. Age and sex differences in critical flicker frequency. *J. exp. Psychol.*, 1947, *37*, 318-332.

Misiak, H. The decrease of critical flicker frequency with age. *Science*, 1951, *113*, 551-552.

Mussen, P. H. & Conger, J. J. *Child development and personality.* New York: Harper, 1956.

Myklebust, H. R. *Auditory disorders in children.* New York: Grune & Stratton, 1954.

Obrist, P. A. Cardiovascular differentiation of sensory stimuli. *Psychosom. Med.*, 1963, *25*, 450-459.

O'Connor, N. Imbecility and color blindness. *Amer. J. ment. Defic.*, 1957, *62*, 83-87.

Ohwaki, S. A developmental study of weight perception—especially on Charpentier's illusion. *Tohoku psychol. Folia*, 1953, *13*, 120-142.

Pascal, G. R. The effect of a disturbing noise on the reaction time of mental defectives. *Amer. J. ment. Defic.*, 1953, *57*, 691-699.

Pascal, G. R., Stolurow, L. M., Zabarenko, R. M., & Chambers, C. S. The delayed reaction in mental defectives. *Amer. J. ment. Defic.*, 1951, *56*, 152-160.

Penrose, L. S. *The biology of mental defect.* New York: Grune & Stratton, 1949.

Pevzner, M. S. Clinical characterization of mentally retarded children. Oligophrenic children. In A. R. Luriya (Ed.), *The mentally retarded child (outlines of studies on the higher nervous activity characteristics of oligophrenic children.)* Washington, D. C.: O.T.S., U. S. Dept. of Commerce, 1963.

Pintner, R. & Anderson, Margaret M. The Muller-Lyer illusion with children and adults. *J. exp. Psychol.*, 1916, *1*, 200-210.

Porteus, S. D. *The Porteus Maze Test and intelligence.* Palo Alto: Pacific Books, 1950.

Porteus, S. D. *The maze test and clinical psychology.* Palo Alto: Pacific Books, 1959.

Raven, J. C. *Guide to using The Coloured Progressive Matrices (1956 Revision).* London: Lewis and Co., 1956.

Razran, G. The observable unconscious and the inferable conscious in current Soviet psychophysiology. *Psychol. Rev.*, 1961, *68*, 81-147.

Reed, G. F. Psychogenic deafness, perceptual defense, and personality variables in children. *J. abn. soc. Psychol.*, 1961, *63*, 663-665.

Reichstein, J. & Rosenstein, J. Differential diagnosis of auditory deficits —a review of the literature. *Except. Child.*, 1964, *31*, 73-82.

Riggs, Margaret M. & Rain, Margaret E. A classification system for the mentally retarded, Part I: Description. *Train. Sch. Bull.*, 1952, *49*, 75-84.

Riggs, Margaret M. & Cassel, Margaret E. A classification system for the mentally retarded, Part II: Reliability. *Train. Sch. Bull.*, 1952, *49*, 151-168.

Rigrodsky, S., Prunty, Frances, & Glovsky, L. A study of the incidence, types and associated etiologies of hearing loss in an institutionalized mentally retarded population. *Train. Sch. Bull.*, 1961, *58*, 30-44.

Ruch, T. C. Neurophysiology in diagnosis. In: *Conference on diagnosis in mental retardation.* Vineland: The Train. Sch., 1958, Pp. 7-26.

Samuels, Ina. Reticular mechanisms and behavior. *Psychol. Bull.*, 1959, *56*, 1-25.

Sarason, S. B. & Gladwin, T. Psychological and cultural problems in mental subnormality: A review of research. In S. B. Sarason, *Psychological problems in mental deficiency.* (3rd ed.) New York: Harper, 1959.

Satter, G. Psychometric scatter among mentally retarded and normal children. *Train. Sch. Bull.*, 1955, *52*, 63-68.

Satter, G. Retarded adults who have developed beyond expectation. Part III: Further analysis and summary. *Train. Sch. Bull.*, 1955, *51*, 237-243.

Satter, G. & Cassel, R. H. Tactual-kinesthetic localization in the mentally retarded. *Amer. J. ment. Defic.*, 1955, *59*, 652-657.

Saunders, D. R. & Schucman, Helen. Syndrome analysis: An efficient procedure for isolating meaningful subgroups in a non-random sample of a population. Paper read at the meeting of the Psychonomic Society, St. Louis, Sept. 1, 1962.

Saxon, Sue V. Differences in reactivity between asphyxial and normal rhesus monkeys. *J. genet. Psychol.*, 1961, *99*, 283-287.

Schlanger, B. B. Speech examination of a group of institutionalized mentally handicapped children. *J. speech hear. Dis.*, 1953, *18*, 339-349.

Schlanger, B. B. *The effects of listening training on the auditory thresholds of mentally retarded children.* Morgantown: West Virginia Univ., 1961.

Schlanger, B. B. & Gottsleben, R. H. Testing the hearing of the mentally retarded. *J. speech hear Dis.*, 1956, *21*, 487-493.

Schucman, Helen, Saunders, D. R., & Thetford, W. N. An application of syndrome analysis to subjects with ulcerative colitis. Paper read at the meeting of the Amer. Psychol. Assoc., St. Louis, Sept. 3, 1962.

Scott, W. S. Reaction time of young intellectual deviates. *Arch. Psychol., N. Y.*, 1940, No. 256.

Semmel, M. I. Arousal theory and vigilance behavior of educable mentally retarded and average children. *Amer. J. ment. Defic.*, 1965, *70*, 38-47.

Semmes, Josephine, Wienstein, S., Ghent, Lila, & Teuber, H.-L. *Somatosensory changes after penetrating brain wounds in man.* Cambridge: Harvard Univ. Press, 1960.

Siegel, M. & Hirschborn, B. Adolescent norms for the Purdue Pegboard Test. *Personnel guid. J.*, 1958, *36*, 563-565.

Simonson, E., Enzer, N., & Blankstein, S. S. The influence of age on the fusion frequency of flicker. *J. exp. Psychol.*, 1941, *29*, 252-255.

Sloan, W. Motor proficiency and intelligence. *Amer. J. ment. Defic.*, 1951, *55*, 394-406.

Spitz, H. H. & Blackman, L. S. The Muller-Lyer illusion in retardates and normals. *Percept. mot. Skills*, 1958, *8*, 219-225.

Spivack, G. & Levine, M. A note on generality of discrimination in life-long brain damage. *Amer. J. ment. Defic.*, 1962, *67*, 473-474.

Spradlin, J. E., Cromwell, R. L., & Foshee, J. G. Studies in activity level: III. Effects of auditory stimulation in organics, familials, hyperactives and hypoactives. *Amer. J. ment. Defic.*, 1960, *64*, 754-757.

Stevens, G. D. & Birch, J. W. A proposal for clarification of the terminology used to describe brain-injured children. *Except. Child.*, 1957, *23*, 346-349.

Stevens, H. A. & Heber, R. (Eds.), *Mental Retardation: A review of research.* Chicago: Univ. of Chicago Press, 1964.

Strauss, A. A., & Lehtinen, Laura E. *Psychopathology and education of the brain-injured child.* New York: Grune & Stratton, 1947.

Strauss, A. A., & Werner, H. The mental organization of the brain-injured-mentally defective child. *Amer. J. Psychiat.*, 1941, *97*, 1195-1203.

Strauss, A. A. & Werner, H. Disorders of conceptual thinking in the brain injured child. *J. nerv. ment. Dis.*, 1942, *96*, 153-172. (a)

Strauss, A. A. & Werner, H. Experimental analysis of the clinical symptom "perseveration" in mentally retarded children. *Amer. J. ment. Defic.*, 1942, *47*, 185-188. (b)

Taylor, J. B. The structure of ability in the lower intellectual range. *Amer. J. ment. Defic.*, 1964, *68*, 766-774.

Teuber, H.-L., Battersby, W. L., & Bender, M. B. *Visual field defects after penetrating missile wounds of the brain.* Cambridge, Mass.: Harvard Univ. Press, 1960.

Thurstone, L. L. & Thurstone, Thelma G. *SRA primary mental abilities for ages 7 to 11. Examiner manual* (2nd ed.), Chicago, Ill.: Science Research Associates, Inc., 1954.

Thurstone, Thelma G. & Thurstone, L. L. *Examiner manual for the SRA primary mental abilities for ages 5 to 7.* Chicago, Ill.: Science Research Associates, Inc., 1953.

Tiffin, J. *Industrial Psychology* (3rd ed.) New York: Prentice-Hall, 1952.

Tiffin, J. & Asher, E. J. The Purdue Pegboard: norms and studies of reliability and validity. *J. appl. Psychol.*, 1948, *32*, 234-247.

Tizard, J., O'Connor, N., & Crawford, J. M. The abilities of adolescent and adult high-grade male defectives. *J. ment. Sci.*, 1950, *96*, 889-907.

Tizord, J. & Venables, P. H. Reaction time responses by schizophrenics, mental defectives and normal adults. *Amer. J. Psychiat.*, 1956, *112*, 803-807.

Tobias, J. & Gorelick, J. The effectiveness of the Purdue pegboard in evaluating work potential of retarded adults. *Train. Sch. Bull.*, 1960, *57*, 94-104.

Tobias, J. & Gorelick, J. The Porteus Maze Test and the appraisal of retarded adults. *Amer. J. ment. Defic.*, 1962, *66*, 600-606.

Tredgold, A. F. *A textbook of mental deficiency.* (7th ed.) Baltimore: Williams and Wilkins, 1947.

Urmer, A. H., Morris, A. B., & Wendland, L. V. The effect of brain damage on Raven's Progressive Matrices. *J. clin. Psychol.*, 1960, *16*, 182-185.

Waisman, H. A. The experimental approach. In F. L. Lyman (Ed.), *Phenylketonuria.* Springfield, Ill.: Charles C Thomas, 1963. Pp. 265-275.

Walters, Anette. A genetic study of geometrical-optical illusions. *Genet. psychol. Monogr.*, 1942, *25*, 101-155.

Wapner, S. & Werner, H. *Perceptual Development.* Worcester, Mass.: Clark Univ. Press, 1957.

Ware, J. R., Baker, R. A., & Sipowicz, R. R. Performance of mental deficients on a simple vigilance task. *Amer. J. ment. Defic.*, 1962, *66*, 647-650.

Wechsler, D. *The measurement of adult intelligence* (3rd ed.) Baltimore: Williams & Wilkins, 1944.

Werner, H. & Strauss, A. A. Types of visuo-motor activity in their relation to low and high performance ages. *Proc. Amer. Assoc. Ment. Defic.*, 1939, *44*, 163-168.

Werner, H. & Strauss, A. A. Causal factors in low performance. *Amer. J. ment. Defic.*, 1940, *45*, 213-218.

Werner, H. & Strauss, A. A. Pathology of figure-background relation in the child. *J. abnorm. soc. Psychol.*, 1941, *36*, 236-248.

Werner, H. & Thuma, B. D. A deficiency in the perception of apparent motion in children with brain injury. *Amer. J. Psychol.*, 1942, *55*, 58-67. (a)

Werner, H. & Thuma, B. D. Critical flicker frequency in children with brain injury. *Amer. J. Psychol.*, 1942, *55*, 394-399. (b)

Whipple, G. M. *Manual of mental and physical tests:* Part I. Simpler processes. Baltimore: Warwick and York, 1914.

Whipple, G. M. *Manual of mental and physical tests:* Part II. Complex Processes. Baltimore: Warwick and York, 1915.

Windle, W. F. Neuropathology of certain forms of mental retardation. *Science*, 1963, *140*, 1186-1189.

Witkin, H. A. & Wapner, S. Visual factors in the maintenance of upright posture. *Amer. J. Psychol.*, 1950, *63*, 31-50.

Woodworth, R. S. *Experimental Psychology.* New York, Holt, 1938.

Woolley, Helen T. *An experimental study of children.* New York: Macmillan, 1926.

Zeaman, D., House, Betty J., & Orlando, R. Use of special training conditions in visual discrimination learning with imbeciles. *Amer. J. ment. Defic.*, 1958, *63*, 453-459.

Zeaman, D. & House, Betty J. The role of attention in retardate discrimination learning. In N. R. Ellis (Ed.), *Handbook of mental deficiency.* New York: McGraw-Hill, 1963, Pp. 159-223.

Zubin, J., Fleiss, J., & Burdock, E. I. Methods for subdividing a population into homogeneous subgroups. Paper read before the seminar on mathematical methods in the social sciences, March 29, 1962.

INDEX